COUSIN JAN

Cousin Jan

ANTONIA RIDGE

FABER & FABER

First published in 1954
First published in this edition 1974
by Faber and Faber Limited
3 Queen Square London W.C.1
Printed in Great Britain by
Whitstable Litho Straker Brothers Ltd
All rights reserved

ISBN 0 571 10513 0

For
OMA and JIM

CONTENTS

Chapter I

WE ALL WENT TO AMSTERDAM

My story begins with my Dutch grandmother—Oma, we called her. She was a sensible, bustling little woman, who believed in godliness, cleanliness, the Royal House of Orange, and families keeping themselves to themselves. In that order. Definitely in that order.

I never set eyes on my grandfather—he died before I was born. So I don't know what he believed in. All I know is that he was of Swedish stock, and that Oma always referred to him with warm, but exasperated, affection, as her "poor Olaf".

He and Oma ran a small bookshop not five minutes' walk from the Queen's palace in Amsterdam. That is, Oma ran it. Poor Olaf not only had no head for business, he was also something of a poet. It seems he used to squander hours and hours blissfully obliging his friends with verses to recite, free of charge, at birthdays, weddings, and funerals, when he ought to have been taking an interest in the shop, of course; especially as Dutch readers have a way of asking searching questions before investing good money in a book. Poor Olaf, torn from his verses, would blink impatiently at an inquiring customer and snort, "What! that book? Good lord, no, I've not read it! But I daresay you'll enjoy it—that is, if you like that sort of thing, of course!"

No; no business-man, our Swedish grandfather.

They had four children, one boy called Piet, and three girls: Anna, Wilhelmina, and Johanna. And when, as Oma put it, three of the four went and married all over the place, she firmly fixed the blame for their flighty behaviour on her poor Olaf, of course.

Piet was the first to take flight. When he was in his early twenties, he saved up for a week's holiday in Paris. And on the very first day, he did what all good Dutchmen do, he set out to take a look at the city from the top of the Eiffel Tower. But the moment he stepped out of the lift, a large straw hat trimmed with cherries blew off a young lady's head and flapped straight in his face. Piet grabbed it, and turned to gaze into the dark grateful eyes of Mademoiselle Yvonne Dupont of Marseilles, who had also travelled to Paris for a week's holiday—but with her Papa and Maman, of course. They were waiting for her at the bottom of the Tower. Maman simply could not endure lifts.

Now Mademoiselle Yvonne was a very pretty girl, so Piet naturally felt he ought to escort her down to join her parents—in case her hat blew off again. And it's a delightfully long way down to the bottom of the Eiffel Tower—if one stops to admire the views as one should. And once on solid earth again, Mademoiselle Yvonne prudently felt she ought to introduce this gallant and good-looking Dutchman to Papa and Maman, now fuming away on a bench in the Champ de Mars, impatiently wondering what on earth any girl could find to stare at all this time from any tower.

And well, that was that. As Maman said later on, it was an absolute thunderbolt of love at first sight.

Piet didn't even return to Amsterdam. He just sent a polite note of farewell to his shipping-company, and seven pages of ecstatic explanation to his dumbfounded family. And spent the rest of his holiday money on a single, third-class railway ticket to Marseilles, where he straightway found a mysterious job that nobody ever really understood, except that it had something to do with eucalyptus and crystallised violets. And six months later, he married his Yvonne, with the full approval and blessing of her sympathetic parents. They also had married outrageously young, so it seemed.

Johanna was the next to startle the family. She went to a friend's wedding and met a tall handsome sailor, a German from Bavaria, by the name of Gottlieb Bauer. And before Oma had time to get her second wind, Johanna was kissing them all good-bye, and was off on a long visit to Gottlieb's mother; whilst Gottlieb nobly signed on for a six months' trip to China to pay for the wedding ring and the furniture.

Then Anna, if you please, was swept off her two sensible feet by an Englishman—a gay, happy-go-lucky fellow with a liking for grey suits, so that he was affectionately known in the bars of Amsterdam as "the mad grey Englishman". But he had one saving grace in Oma's eyes. He at least had an excellent job right there in Amsterdam. More satisfactory still, Anna and her Englishman speedily presented Oma with two bouncing grandchildren—first my sister, and then me.

It was then that Oma decided the time had come to learn a little useful English; and by the time we were toddling round she had mastered a unique collection of brisk commands to juveniles, such as:

Do dat door open wide please!

Do dis door shut quiet please!

Where is your hant-car-chiff?

Och! Och! Bodder-me-not-even-now!

It was not until years later, however, that I realised that "Bodder-me-not-even-now!" was Oma's English for "Don't bother me just now!"

Then, quite suddenly, our young English father, bored with his good steady job in Amsterdam, decided to return to his native land. And one grey November morning, our Oma, white but not tearful, waved off our little family to foreign shores as well.

A month later, to everyone's relief and pleasure, Wilhelmina kindly fell in love with a Dutchman, a sober squarish young man called Hendricus, but known to his family and friends as Henk, of course.

And Henk was not only all-Dutch to the backbone, he was also interested in books, selling them, that is. And as soon as they were married, he moved in and began to help Oma in her bookshop.

Well, as the years went by, Oma gradually acquired other grandchildren, of course. And, as Oma so often sighed, a queer mixed bunch we were, too: three of us over there in England, one in Germany, two in France, and only three where we all ought to have been—in Holland.

I'll never forget the time we nine first met. It was the year Oma celebrated her sixtieth birthday. The Dutch set great store on birthdays, and that year Oma set her heart on having us all there, especially the children. For weeks and weeks we lived in a whirl of letters till everything was settled to the last detail. And I still recall our shrieks of delight when my mother read out her last-minute letter from Amsterdam which announced that it was the grown-ups who were going to be billeted on sympathetic friends and neighbours, and that we grandchildren, all nine of us, were to sleep in Oma's house.

We were the last to arrive, I remember. And Oma's tall house seemed to be swarming with strange excitable aunts and uncles all talking and laughing at once as they kissed and hugged us and exclaimed on our size and remarkable likeness to this one or that one. And there was a rich warm smell of cigar-smoke and eau-de-Cologne and coffee, and there in the middle of it all was our Oma, short, stout, dressed in black silk, crying and laughing, and issuing orders right and left, to which somebody must have listened, for presently all the luggage was stored somewhere or the other, and there we were, all nine grandchildren, sitting round the kitchen table with strict instructions to finish up every crumb of a mountain of bread and butter, three sorts of cold sliced sausage, two sorts of cheese, a stack of gingerbread, and a boiled egg each, whilst our parents and Oma ate and talked in the living-room.

At first we reached for the bread and butter in stiffest silence, eyeing each other, sorting ourselves out.

Those two dark boys with long white socks and comic floppy bow-ties were Paul and Philippe from Marseilles, of course.

The three plump girls with long fair plaits and solemn blue eyes were the Amsterdammers: Rika, Mina and Toje.

And the tall boy with the big hands and feet, freckles, yellow hair cut short like a brush all over his head, and dancing blue eyes, must be Jan, Jan from Germany. Oma and all other foreign relations called him Yon, but we Britons took no notice of that. Nobody could convince us that J-A-N spelt Yon in any language.

Indeed I was thinking of this when Jan caught me staring at him; and gave me a slow deliberate wink, as if to say, "Funny, aren't we?"

I giggled. That did it. We all began to giggle, and then to laugh, for we *were* funny, painfully, unbearably funny, just sitting there, eating, and staring at each other.

Then up shot Jan, draped a tea-towel over his shoulders, and said in very bad Dutch, "Look, look, cousins! I am our Oma!"

And he began to walk round the table, patting our heads, wiping our noses, and smacking our bottoms, till we were all rolling on our chairs with laughter.

Then up jumped Philippe and yelled, "Et moi, je suis Tanta Joh!" And he stuffed the roller-towel up his jacket— our Tanta Joh was a fine figure of a woman—and he began to caper round the table, too.

Five minutes later we were all parading ·round the kitchen in a first-class game of our own invention called, "The Meeting of the Parents" with Jan standing on the mangle shouting the orders. And such were our shrieks in four languages that Oma came rushing in.

"Potvordikkie!" she cried, plainly delighted to see the ice so well and truly shattered. But Oma was never the one to allow pleasure to dictate to commonsense, so she promptly set us to work to clear the table in the living-room, whilst our parents grandly retired to the sitting-room to drink their coffee and get on with their talking.

It was then that Jan invented our second party-game: the "Licking-out-of-the-Glasses".

I didn't think much of this one. I didn't care for the taste of anything left at the bottom of any of the glasses, even the thick yellow stuff which Paul swore was called Advocaat because it set everyone talking away like a lawyer, and a French one at that.

I did not let Great Britain down however—I came in third with six glasses licked out.

France won the contest. Philippe had polished off thirteen glasses as clean as a whistle; and Jan hoisted him up on the mangle and shouted, "Behold him! The First Prize! The Champion!"

And we all clapped and cheered, and Philippe bowed, and kissed the tips of his fingers to us, precisely like a real conjuror on a real stage, better in fact.

Then Oma came back.

"Bed!" she said. "Ja, ja, bett! Oui, oui, mes enfants, lit! Come! Venez! Komm!"

We followed her up the narrow twisting stairs to a large bedroom. There, pushed close together, were three beds for the four boys, three quite ordinary beds, one large and two small.

But we girls, oh, we five girls were the lucky ones! We were to sleep in the attic. The ATTIC. And on camp-beds, genuine, romantic, heavenly camp-beds. In the ATTIC!

When the excitement had died down a little, Oma called for silence, and made a little speech. She said she wanted us all to enjoy ourselves. She wanted us to have a holiday we would remember all our lives long. But now we must be quiet. No more shouting. No more games. Indeed she was going to trust us to be quiet. And, of course, she knew she could trust us to be most careful with our candles. But above all, she wanted us to say our prayers to the dear Lord in Heaven above who had gathered us together safely under her roof. And by the way, she and our parents were now going to drink still more coffee with a neighbour called Mevrouw Vos who lived three doors away. We'd hardly be lonely, eh? All the same, we would know where to run

17

if something unexpected did happen. And Oma kissed us all goodnight, and went downstairs.

"Now!" said Jan. "Now, what have I for a fine ideal Bitte, setzt Euch!"

He sat down on the attic-floor, and waved to us to be seated, too. So we all sat down, and looked at him.

"Well?" asked my brother William. "What's the fine idea?"

Jan fumbled in his pocket, and pulled out a handful of whistles, nine little whistles, the sort you could buy for a penny each in those days.

Somebody laughed.

"These," said Jan, suddenly very stiff, "these are not for fun. They are . . . they are . . . Look! Please look!"

He handed us each a whistle. And when we examined them, we saw that every little whistle had a figure nine scratched on it, very clear and sharp.

Then Jan struggled for words, and we helped him out. Yes, in German, Dutch, English and French we got down to it, till presently there it shone—Jan's fine idea, Jan's wonderful idea.

We nine were to BACK EACH OTHER UP, not only all through this holiday, but all our lives long. These whistles were to be our secret family badge, never to be used lightly but only in times of peril. Yes, from that evening on, if one of us was in trouble, he knew he had only to blow his whistle, and the rest of us would fly to the rescue.

"Now, we must swear!" said Jan; and raised his right hand.

So we all raised our right hands and swore. And there we sat for a moment, very still and silent in the candlelight.

The sound of voices below broke the spell. It was our parents calling goodnight to us before they went out on a gust of laughter and talk, banging the street-door behind them.

"Komm!" said Jan, and rose to his feet, beckoning to the boys to follow him. And so solemn was our mood that they almost tiptoed out, through the door, and down the narrow attic-stairs.

Then we five girls began to undress. That is my sister and I began to tear off our clothes in our usual carefree way, and we were most surprised to observe that our three Dutch cousins had obviously been trained to undress in the most circumspect manner, using their long nightdresses as tents. And our eyes nearly popped out of our heads when they presently unfolded spotless white drawers, and hoisted them up under their nightdresses. And thus chastely attired, they blew out our candle, and knelt down to say their prayers.

And I remember lying there in the strange Dutch moonlight slanting through the sky-light, thinking with infinite compassion of my best friends over there in England. They had ordinary English grandmothers. They went to places like Weston or Bournemouth for their holidays. And I saw them growing green with envy as I told them about Oma, the attic, the camp-beds, and the whistles.

Well, maybe not the whistles. I resolved to *try* not to tell them about the whistles. I felt Oma would approve of this unselfish decision.

Suddenly, all five of us shot up in our camp-beds. Those boys were up to something! We could hear a frantic flurry of bare feet racing down the stairs, and voices urgently encouraging somebody to speed and endurance.

"Good! Good! We arrive! We arrive!" sang out Paul's voice.

"I bet Jan's had another good idea," said my sister wistfully.

"But they promised to be quiet," said Mina, outraged. "They promised no more games to-night! They promised!"

We listened intently. Doors banged, voices called, there was a burst of distant cheering, and then feet came padding up the stairs again, and into the bedroom below. One pair however came racing up our attic-stairs; there was a gentlemanly knock on our door, then it opened inch by inch. And there stood Jan.

"Did you hear?" he breathed. "It was the First Prize! Sick! But we raced him to the water-closet just in time. He feels fine now. Quite hungry, in fact."

"So do we," said my sister.

"Good!" said Jan. "Here, catch!"

And he threw us each a bar of chocolate, beautiful strange German chocolate.

"Oh, Jan!" I said. "Du bist . . . Du bist . . ."

"All right?" suggested Jan.

"Ja!" I said. "Ja! Du bist all right, Cousin Jan!"

"Fine!" breathed Jan, his face suddenly radiant.

Then he turned, and fairly flew down the attic-stairs.

"Why," I thought, "he *wants* us to like him!"

And very touched, I began to eat my chocolate, taking the very smallest bites so as to make it last as long as possible.

Chapter II

JAN HAS A FINE IDEA

After the long planning, the careful scraping together of the money to travel all the way to Amsterdam, our parents naturally thought they had every right to enjoy themselves. And they did! Heavens, how they talked! Long, long after we had been packed off to bed, we would hear them still at it. Not that it bothered us. On the contrary, it all added to the lofty pleasure of sleeping in our attic, high above the talk, the singing, and the laughter. It made us feel superior, and safe, all at once.

And sometimes when a door was left open, we would catch the happy, eager voice of our Oma:

> *"Now listen, Joh, tell me . . .*
> *Anna, my love, tell me.*
> *Piet, my son, tell me."*

And we'd smile benevolently at each other and say, "There goes Oma again, catching up with the news!"

Then I remember, too, that it puzzled me to notice that the merrier the party, the sadder grew the songs of our jovial Uncle Gottlieb. I would sometimes wake to hear his rich deep voice singing: "Schön ist die Jugend! Lovely is youth, so lovely is youth, but it comes no more, it comes no more!"

And I would fall asleep again wondering why on earth this seemed to depress him. Wasn't he down there, staying up as late as he pleased, eating, drinking, making merry and smoking cigars, in short, doing just the very things so sternly forbidden to lovely youth at any hour of the night? Was his memory then so short; or were things different when he was young?

But no matter how late these parties broke up, Oma was always downstairs bright and early of a morning to give us our breakfast—queer Dutch breakfasts with cheese with caraway seeds in it which we called mosquito-cheese, three or four kinds of sausages, raw bacon sliced wafer-thin, and gingerbread. All of which we speared with a fork and ate on slice after slice of bread and butter.

Then when we girls had washed up and made the beds, and the boys had cleaned the knives and all the shoes, Oma would inspect hands, ears, necks and handkerchiefs, and march us into her sitting-room to learn to say the Lord's Prayer in decent Dutch, and to sing two Dutch national hymns.

The first began:

> *Wilhelmus of Nassau,*
> *Of Teutonic blood am I . . .*

The second was odder still, for us, I mean, for it began:

> *None but Netherlands blood in our veins,*
> *Free from foreign taint.*

But we sang away with gusto, never bothering our young heads about our varied foreign taints. Indeed, I don't think we would ever have inquired into Wilhelmus and his Teutonic blood, if Oma hadn't insisted on enlightening us. She said that Wilhelmus, though born in Germany, had done his heroic best to make up for that. He had devoted all he had, life itself, to the cause of Holland. "And moreover," said Oma very significantly, "our beloved hero was known as 'William the Silent'!"

Somewhat subdued by Oma's relish for silent heroism, we would then go on to tackle a collection of poems about Holland being our dear, our native land, though exiled we were on foreign strand. And Oma would explain that these beautiful poems had been written by our Swedish grandfather at the special request of a friend who had sailed away to take up a very fine job in Java. And Oma, blowing her nose, would say that she bitterly regretted it now, of course, but at the time she hadn't thought much of these poems, what with the annual stock-taking round the corner and the bills pouring in, and her poor Olaf scribbling away, deaf to all entreaties to lend a hand. And little had our Oma dreamt how handy these poems would come in one day—and for their very own grandchildren, too!

Very touched, we would then positively slave to do poetic justice to poor Olaf, and presently, beaming with pleasure at our application, Oma would cry, "Fine! Fine!" And proceed to hand out packages of sandwiches and sixpence each to cover all expenses, and send us out to see the sights of Amsterdam—in charge of the three Amsterdammers naturally, and with strict orders to visit museums and churches if it came on to rain, not to speak to strangers except clergymen, policemen, and tram-conductors, and to be home at six sharp for our good, cooked meal which she called "Evening Bread".

But as soon as we were out, and tearing along the banks of the canals, quite smoothly and easily, it was always Jan who took charge.

Jan Has a Fine Idea

"Listen, listen! Now what have I for a fine idea!"

And we would listen willingly, for Jan's ideas were always fine, indeed at times they were absolutely entrancing —at least, we thought so.

There was, for instance, his idea for Oma's birthday.

Now all that day in true Dutch style, Oma, in her best silk dress, had done nothing but welcome friends and neighbours who called in to offer her their hearty felicitations together with a little gift—a bunch of flowers, a plant, a book, or a lace mat to go under one of her many ornaments. And Oma, in return, offered each caller a little light refreshment, so that all that day long we girls, with pinafores over our best dresses, were kept busy washing up coffee cups and glasses, whilst the boys politely fetched and carried chairs, and ushered in, and sped each smiling well-wisher.

Toward six that evening there was a lull in the stream of callers, and Oma said, "Well, there won't be anyone else for an hour or so. So we'll eat, too. But where are those children?"

At that very moment, the sitting-room door flew open, and in we marched, faces shining, hair neatly combed, and bearing a great basket of flowers decorated with little paper flags of Holland, France, Germany and England. With solemn ceremony we set this down, and bowed to Oma. Then, at a signal from Jan, we took a deep breath and began to chant a poem in Dutch that we had made up between us, and which ran roughly on these lyrical lines:

> *Our Grandpapa Olaf, at any time,*
> *Could take up his pen and write wishes in rhyme.*
> *We nine grandchildren wish that we*
> *Were only half as clever as he.*

But still we'll try, Oma dear,
To make our birthday wishes clear.

So hail to our Oma
From her grandchildren nine!
If we only had money,
We'd give her jewels so fine!

Here, the boys whipped out mouth-organs and combs covered with paper, and we girls lifted up our voices, and off we went on a melody that we knew would go straight to our Oma's patriotic heart.

Holland is a lovely land,
Yet once it was but sea and sand!
Land with toil and love created,
Pearl of lands, from sea translated,
Meadows, cities, dunes, and strand,
Holland is a lovely land!

Holland is a lovely land,
Triumph dear of heart and hand,
From distant shores men come to stare,
Respectfully they all declare,
Holland is a wonderland!
Holland is a lovely land.

Then, seeing the tears in our Oma's kind eyes, we flung down mouth-organs and combs, and rushed to embrace her, half-smothering her in our eighteen loving arms, deafening her with our shouts of, "Hearty felicitations! Live many, many years more, Oma!"

Yes, that was one of Jan's finest ideas, one that we were to remember all our lives long.

Then there was the day we went to the Rijksmuseum.

Now every visitor to Amsterdam pays at least one visit to the Rijksmuseum to see Rembrandt's great masterpiece known as "The Night Watch". And in those days, before it was cleaned up, it was indeed nocturnal—a dark and splendid confusion of bearded officers rapping out orders, lesser ranks enthusiastically loading and firing off muskets, and youths and boys having the time of their lives walloping drums or waving pikes. And every man and boy of them dressed to please himself—feathers waving in round hats, tall hats, wavy-brimmed hats; fine linen ruffs, rich satin sashes, elegant high boots, grand embroidered waistcoats, and stockings all the colours of the rainbow.

Now, as luck would have it, the day we nine tiptoed into the vast silent hall where this masterpiece hangs, there, before it, stood a large party in charge of a guide, and all listening earnestly to his explanations in Dutch, English, French and German.

Led by Jan, we wormed our way to the fore, and listened, too.

When the guide paused to take breath, a Frenchman standing close to us, muttered, "Ah, non! C'est écrasant!"

Philippe, in a loud ringing voice, obligingly translated.

"Monsieur thinks it's crushing!"

"Veux-tu te taire!" growled the ungrateful Frenchman.

The guide, deaf as a post, hastily called our attention to the dog in the picture, pointing out that this reaction to the roll of a drum has remained unchanged through countless canine generations. Everybody smiled and nodded; and the party moved off.

But Jan waved to us to stay where we were. And as soon as they were out of sight, he pointed to a dashing gentleman, dressed in sparkling yellow with a white feather in his tall hat, swaggering away in the foreground of the picture.

"That one!" he hissed. "You see him? That one is ME!"

"Et moi!" came in Paul, quick as a flash. "Je suis ce type-là!" And he pointed to another fine gentleman in silver and green.

That did it. In less than five minutes we had shared out all the outstanding personalities in the picture between us, not without much whispered argument, of course.

I ruthlessly bagged the little girl in the masterpiece—a plump little girl dressed in yellow satin with pearls and blue feathers adorning her fair hair. She carries a silver goblet in her hands, and more entrancing still, from her waist dangle a dagger, a pistol, a pouch, and, believe it or not, a fat white chicken with its legs tied together. Oh, a queen among little girls, wearing just the get-up I would have chosen myself if I'd only had the chance. And up at dead of night, too, enjoying herself with the best!

Presently, when it was clearly understood who was who in the masterpiece, we gave a last affectionate look at our other more glorious selves; and then set off to track down the guide and his party.

We found them standing in front of a majestic marble bust.

"Now this," the guide was saying, "this, ladies and gentlemen, is our Admiral van Tromp, who defeated the British Navy at the Battle of the Downs."

The French gentleman then asked something which we couldn't catch.

"Ah, no, monsieur!" smiled back the guide. "I regret it infinitely, for it would be an excellent story to tell. But I cannot swear that it was at this battle that the British ran out of ammunition, and the Dutch boarded their vessels and kindly sold them cannon-balls and powder—at a hand-some profit, so that they might all get on with the battle! Ha-ha-ha!

"But it is certainly true," continued the guide, when the laughter died down, "that after this great victory Admiral van Tromp tied a broom to his masthead to show he was sweeping the British off the seas. Ha-ha-ha!"

The party obediently laughed again; and then they all straggled off once more.

My brother William, however, crimson with patriotic fury, fumbled in his pocket, pulled out his mouth-organ, and glaring up at the haughty Admiral van Tromp, began to blow "Rule Britannia!" very loud and defiant.

We gaped, speechless.

But quick as a flash Jan grabbed the mouth-organ, and waved frantically. "Scatter!" he rapped. "Scatter up in little crumbs!"

We understood. When the keeper came panting round the corner, we had scattered all over that great hall, every one of us standing close to some convenient grown-up, pretending to belong to them, peering studiously with them into nine distant glass-cases.

The keeper glared about him, and shot off again, down the corridor, and out of sight. From the corner of our eyes we watched Jan saunter away. One by one, at cautious intervals, we followed him—along the corridor, down the grand staircase, through the great door, across the road, and into the park.

And there we let rip! Round and round we tore, exulting. William from England had had the reckless courage to speak his mind about old van Tromp and his broom, but we had rescued him! In the face of fearful odds, we had rescued him! We nine, we were victorious! Hip-pip-victorious!

Breathless, we flung ourselves down on the grass round our favourite bench; and began to devour our sandwiches.

It was then that I happened to say that in my glass-case I had seen a queer old letter, with a flowery border all round it, and written in very queer old English. Yes, English. And I told them about it as best I could. My Dutch was never good.

"Ach! I understand!" cried Jan, and shot to his feet, eyes sparkling. "Ja, ja, I understand everything! In this letter, the noble Duke of York in England, to a black savage king sends best greetings . . ."

"No!" I objected. "It just said 'to the King of Ardra'!"

"And," rushed on Jan, taking no notice whatever, "this noble Duke of York to the black savage king writes, 'Ah! so you welcome our English white traders, eh? Good! England very pleased with you! So here is one fine bed, and one fine crown. The bed is to sleep in. The crown is to wear on your head, just as by our King of England, Scotland, France and Ireland.

"'But, remember, if for your dinner you think to EAT our white traders, then PASS-AUF!

"'We will come and take back this fine bed and this fine crown. And klaps-klaps! Klaps and schwaps!'"

And Jan danced round and round, walloping and whacking an unseen horde of ungrateful cannibals.

"Gosh, no!" I shrieked. "It didn't say all that. It just said . . ."

"And this," roared Jan, "gives me one fine idea. Listen!"

In less than ten minutes, we were divided into two teams: Four White Traders versus Five Black Savages.

Jan, of course, was the King of Ardra. His royal bed was our park bench; and we plaited our nine handkerchiefs together to make his royal crown.

William was the noble Duke of York. We felt we owed him this.

The game began with a complicated sort of hide-and-seek. If we Black Savages won, we lolled victoriously on the royal bed, whilst the White Traders bit the dust at our feet and howled for mercy.

If the White Traders won, they tore off Jan's royal crown, and sprawled all over his royal bed, whilst we Black Savages grovelled flat on our stomachs, wailing away, till the noble Duke graciously consented to pardon us.

But all this racing and yelling was thirsty work, of course, so presently we tore to the fountain for a long drink. And then we boarded a tramcar for a shop we had discovered in a back street behind a large post-office.

Now this shop was rather like a fish and chip shop in England, but instead of fish and chips it sold tiny dough-nuts, called "poffertjes". And the man who stood all day long behind the shining brass counter frying these dough-nuts, always served them up in a white, pointed bag, dusted them with fine sugar, and slapped a lump of butter on top.

And there we would stand, dipping each "poffertje" into a tiny sea of butter, blissfully burning our fingers and tongues, and every now and then one of the Dutch girls would say "Lecker?" And we would nod and sigh, "Ja! ja!" for they were indeed delicious, absolutely wonderful.

But the "poffertjes" were not the end of that perfect day.

On our way home, we decided to push our way through the busiest street in all Amsterdam—the Kalverstraat. It was very narrow—it still is, with shop after shop on either side. And we dodged in and out of the crowds and the bicycles; and William was just saying he bet their Lord Mayor or somebody had passed a law that all Amster-dammers had to go out shopping on their bicycles, and that only those with punctures were allowed on the tramcars, when Jan shouted something that must have meant, "Let's get out of here!" for he wheeled sharp right, and led the way up a little alley.

The din, the hubbub, died behind us. And there, to the right, we saw a lovely old gateway built of bricks the colour of wild raspberries.

And this led into another little alley.

"Regardez!" whispered Philippe, and pointed to a notice on the wall.

> *Here, man must not cycle.*
> *Children must not play.*
> *Tradesmen must not push carts.*
> *Walking only is permitted.*

So we walked, as permitted, down the alley . . . and straight into another world, a quiet corner of old Holland, just as Rembrandt himself must have known it. Great trees, smooth green lawns, and set all round them, tall ancient houses, no two of them alike. Not a soul about, not a sound save the twittering of the birds.

"Almshouses," explained Mina. "For the old."

And there, too, for the old, were two little churches, one Catholic, one Protestant, looking at each other in the friendliest way.

The most tranquil, the most gentle, the loveliest place in which to be old!

Jan pointed to the sparrows hopping about on the grass.

"Old, too!" he declared. "Only old birds permitted here."

We gazed at them. And yes, these sparrows *were* different. They were hopping about in the most civil and orderly way. They, too, must have retired here to spend a quiet old age.

Then Jan pointed to one of the houses, one with its little front garden bright with sunflowers.

"That one! You see it? That one is for me, when I am old."

So we all selected a house each for our aged selves.

"And then," decided Jan, "we must all have a cycle each with three big safe wheels."

"Man must not cycle here!" objected my sister.

"Other men, it means," said Jan firmly. "Not us."

"For us olds," said Philippe, "everything will be permitted."

"Of course," said Jan. "So, look!"

From the gateway of his house he wheeled an imaginary tricycle, carefully dusted three invisible and very large wheels, mounted an imaginary saddle, rang an imaginary bell, and rode off.

So we all climbed on imaginary tricycles too. And our aged selves pedalled after him, past the little churches, round all the almshouses, down the little alley, through the lovely brick gateway, and into the other alley.

Suddenly, viciously, the din of the Kalverstraat came roaring towards us. Our tricycles vanished. Nothing was old and gentle and quiet any more. We were children again; and very tired, and hot, and hungry.

And there before us lay that noisy, crowded shopping-street—all those people, all those bicycles.

"Oh, come on!" said William crossly. And this time, he led the way.

Jan walked behind me. I could hear him dragging his feet.

When I turned, he waved an angry hand.

"All this!" he said. "Wie furchtbar!"

"Ja!" I said. "Awful!"

And not another word did we say all the way home.

Chapter III

ALONG THE GRACHTS OF
AMSTERDAM

When we got home that evening, there was Oma, apron about waist, waiting to dish up our supper, and very eager to know where we had been and what we had seen.

And at the very sight of her we felt better. There was always something so comfortable about coming home to Oma. She trusted us. She never fussed. She saw to it that we, too, enjoyed ourselves pretty much as we pleased, as long as we turned up safe, sound, and hungry; and were asleep, or at least quiet, at a reasonable hour.

So as a grateful quid-pro-quo we saw to it that we at least gazed each day upon three or four of the better known sights of Amsterdam, knowing that we would only have to rattle off their names, and Oma would be delighted to talk away about them whilst we got on with our eating.

At first, our French aunt—Tante Von-von, we called her—was half-inclined to be restive about all this. She liked to have her Paul and Philippe one each side of her, hair beautifully combed and with their gloves on. They were handsome boys, and she adored hearing people exclaim how nice they looked.

"But, Von-von," said our clever Oma, "you and Piet deserve a good holiday, a real change. Leave all the children to me. Safety in numbers, you know! Let them have this fine chance to get to know each other. I promise you they will be all right."

And, of course, we *were* all right. Moreover, with no well-meaning grown-ups to embarrass us, we really did get to know each other; and in our own curious fashion we also got to know the city of Amsterdam. Indeed, no organised sightseeing, with a conscientious adult in charge, could ever have given us so rich and diverting a crop of memories. Even now, after all these years, I have only to stroll under the trees of some quiet back-street of Amsterdam, and the magic of that distant holiday comes crowding in on me, tugging at my memory; and I see again, very clear and bright, the real high-lights of that youthful sight-seeing, the first-rate moments which we never once disclosed— even to Oma.

There was that hot sunny day, for instance, when we set out to take a cool shady walk along the "grachts" of the city. Oma had carefully explained to us that canals flowed from one Dutch town to another, but that the grachts were the ancient waterways of the city itself; and very convenient, too, in the restful days of old when tradesmen used sensible, quiet boats to deliver their goods.

Oma admitted that there were grachts *and* grachts, just as there were roads *and* roads. So there was no sense in inspecting the shabby, smelly ones, especially on such a stifling day. Our Dutch cousins were therefore directed to escort us along such fine, stately waterways as the Heeren or Gentlemen's Gracht, the Prinsen or Princes' Gracht, and the Keizers or Emperors' Gracht.

After this, Oma suggested we made our way to the Zoological Gardens, the oldest and most beautiful in the world, where we could improve our minds in the shade; and also inspect a most romantic, artificial ruin, absolutely like a real one in a book—moat, ivy, owls and all.

So off we went and obediently wandered under the lovely old elm trees growing along these statelier grachts. And William, eyeing the patrician houses lining their banks, said if we were a Gentleman or a Prince or an Emperor, he'd jolly well live in Park Lane over in London where his high-born children could nip over a good safe road, and listen to the orators arguing away like mad in Hyde Park.

Whereas, said William darkly, he bet any number of high-born Dutch infants had nipped out of their prams, toddled over, and splash! were drowned in these grachts with never a bubble to mark the spot. And William, warming to his grisly theme, said he for one would loathe to go fishing in any gracht.

Our Dutch cousins were hotly disputing all this, when over a nearby bridge, came a most interesting procession, and cut short the argument.

Arm in arm with a red-faced gentleman walked a lady in a bright blue costume carrying a tight bunch of white carnations. Behind, two by two, walked all their relations and friends, grown-ups, half-grown-ups, and children too.

"Fine!" breathed Jan. "Come on!"

He tore ahead, and at a discreet distance began to walk behind the procession, waving to us to follow him.

So we formed twos, and fell in behind him. Nobody turned round; so nobody spotted us.

All along one gracht we paced, over a bridge, down another gracht, across another bridge, and there, flowing into an important-looking building, were three or four other processions, very like ours.

"The Stadhuis!" whispered Mina. "And it's free to-day."

"What is?"

"Weddings, of course!"

Our procession was now politely slowing down to give right of way to another one, not nearly so well-dressed as ours, we were gratified to see. Then off we set again, and yes, *we* were bound for the Stadhuis, too!

Through a great door we went, and turned into a crowded room. I counted seven ladies clutching flowers, and milling all about them, shaking hands and exchanging greetings, all their joyous families and friends.

"Stand here!" hissed Jan. "And smile!"

He grouped us discreetly between two of the more excited wedding-parties, counting, of course, that each would assume that we belonged to the other. And there we stood for a moment, beaming to right and to left, till a gentleman came in, and loudly requested us to be kind enough to proceed into another room across the corridor. So we all formed up again, and off we went, all nine of us safely wedged between our two unsuspecting parties.

In this second large room, behind a long table, sat a row of solemn gentlemen. And all seven brides and their grooms lined up in pairs before this table, families and friends massed behind them. Now we may have been uninvited, but our behaviour was irreproachable. We made no attempt whatever to worm our way to the fore, but prudently remained well in the background. Indeed, there were two such well-built ladies in front of me that I had my work cut out to remain unobtrusive and yet see something of what was going on. What I did see sent me squirming round to take a look at my sister. And yes, her eyes were popping out of her head, too! I conveyed to her that I couldn't believe it either. But it was true! The most important gentleman behind the table was now standing up, and he was marrying all seven couples at one go!

With seven voices that spoke as one, all seven grooms boomed, "Ja!"

In timid chorus, all seven brides swore to be true.

And taking up a little hammer, the gentleman rapped smartly on the table, and declared them all well and truly married.

He then made a little speech, but the two ladies in front of me were now looking in their handbags for handkerchiefs to wipe their eyes, so my attention was too divided to catch more than a sentence or two. But I gathered the gentleman was warning the seven brides and their grooms that marriage was not all sweet roses and sunshine, they must sensibly expect a few thorns and a thundercloud or two as well.

Then, quite suddenly, it was all over; and there were Jan and the others edging their way towards the door. A moment later we were blinking in the hot sunshine beating down on the pavement outside.

"Listen!" pleaded my sister. "Let's wait and watch them all come out."

"Why?" objected William. "They'll look the same."

But William was wrong. Each procession as it filed through the door now looked positively triumphant, and each groom proudly carried a book in his free hand.

"Marriage book," explained Rika.

And this marriage book, it appeared, was far better than an ordinary wedding certificate, for it had twelve blank pages on which to enter all the names and birthdays of the children. And when they'd filled them all up, the Lord Mayor kindly gave them another book—free of charge.

But, by now, the boys had had enough of weddings, so we set course for the Zoological Gardens. And as I dawdled behind the others, I decided I would get married in the Stadhuis myself one day. All along the grachts of Amsterdam I would pace, arm in arm with my new husband, and followed by all my admiring family and friends in their Sunday best and with buttonholes of white carnations.

And I'd straightway fill up every page of my first marriage book, I would. Six boys I would have, with manly straight hair and sensible short English names, and six girls with long fair curls right down to their waists, and romantic Dutch names. And so pay my respects to both sides of the family.

And a prime childhood they were going to have, my twelve children. I was going to be just like Oma, I was. Every day, knapsacks on backs, I would send them out exploring. And when winter came, every head in Holland would turn to admire my twelve children skating along the frozen canals in a beautiful straight line in order of size— just like the children on a calendar Oma had sent us one Christmas.

Bands playing, spectators cheering, on, on would skate my twelve children, and win every prize. And I was just about to buy them a gold watch each to commemorate this shining victory, when, "Oh, come on!" yelled eight exasperated voices. And there were the others massed on a distant bridge, howling to me to hurry.

We "did" the artificial ruin and the animals in the Zoological Gardens in record time. As William said, ruins and lions simply look like ruins and lions any old where.

We then settled down under a tree near a beautiful lake to eat our sandwiches. Presently, Heaven only knows how, the conversation drifted round to boxing, of all subjects!

And Paul and Philippe claimed that real old-fashioned French boxing, La Boxe Française, was far more palpitating than all other sorts. No gloves were worn, and one was permitted to use the feet as well as the fists.

And Paul and Philippe had once watched a picked team of the older boys in their school demonstrating this Boxe Française up on a platform, with a monitor in front calling out the numbers.

William, most sarcastic, said that must have been a sight, twenty boys bashing each other to numbers.

And Philippe and Paul, between them, hotly retorted that La Boxe Française wasn't brutal British or American boxing where one champion is paid to try to batter the senses out of another. The noble Boxe Française was only used in self-defence. One had to wait patiently until face to face with a brigand who demanded your money or your life. Then, garde! Up went one's fists! And oop! Up went one's left foot and kicked him smartly on the knee. And as the brigand strove to dodge that, oop! Up went one's right foot and kicked him the knock-out, slap under the chin. Down crashed the brigand, and all the gendarmes had to do was sling him on a stretcher and carry him off to the prison hospital.

And when William could get a word in, he urged them to come back to those twenty boys boxing away to numbers up on a platform. Philippe patiently explained they were just *demonstrating* the way they would kick, punch and parry if only given the chance to tackle a brigand. And the way their arms and legs had shot up and down in perfect

40

time, absolutely as one boxer, one would have sworn they were twenty clockwork boys pulverising twenty invisible brigands.

"Come on! Show us the movements!" said William, deeply interested now.

So all the boys got up and began to practise the noble Boxe Française.

But we girls, very bored indeed, went down to the water's edge to offer the crusts from our sandwiches to the lovely birds wading on long pink legs between the lily leaves floating on the cool green water.

Chapter IV

EXCURSION TO CLEVES

Now, as I recall this distant holiday, I remember how my father once declared that he had yet to meet a family to equal ours when it came to celebrating. He said it was far more than a natural bent. To his mind we had a positive gift for organising birthdays, feast-days, funerals, weddings of every kind, and all other outings with a good meal at the end of them. And to prove this, he'd quote his Uncle Jim's silver-wedding day.

Now Uncle Jim really was my father's uncle—a large, genial Englishman who had spent nearly all his life in Holland, and who had also married a Dutch woman—our Tanta Marta.

Tanta Marta was a tiny managing woman who fussed round our solid, six-foot uncle for all the world like a bossy little tug-boat scurrying round a battleship. Moreover, having no children of her own to clutter up her judgment, she was forever pointing out what was wrong in the way we were all being brought up.

But I must be fair. Tanta Marta was also a generous woman, who shared all Oma's views on the sacred obligations of family ties. And that year, on the last day but one of our holiday, Tanta Marta and Uncle Jim were to celebrate their silver wedding-day.

It was enthusiastically agreed that the occasion called for something outstanding, something red-letter in family celebrations. As Oma said, there we all were for once, right on the spot, ready to offer heartiest felicitations; and only too eager to help Tanta Marta and Uncle Jim enjoy themselves. My father, far too earnestly, said yes, indeed; he, for one, would gladly help Uncle Jim to set out the best flower-pots. Oma didn't seem to think much of this, for "setting out the flower-pots" is the Dutch way of saying painting the town red.

But Oma was even less enthusiastic when Tanta Marta called in one evening and formally invited us all to go with them on an excursion to Cleves on the auspicious date, all expenses to be met by Uncle Jim.

Oma, deeply shocked, said she had never in all her life heard of anyone going away on their silver-wedding day. One was definitely expected to stay home to receive all one's friends and neighbours, and then wind up the festivities with a grand family party at night.

What would everyone think when they knocked that day at Tanta Marta's door, and received no reply?

Tanta Marta tartly retorted she was of course sending polite cards all round in good time to warn people they would not be home on the great day. And as one was expected to keep open house for fourteen whole days *before* the silver-wedding day, everybody would just have to have the common sense to come along some time during that preliminary fortnight to drink their health and offer their good wishes.

In any case, our Uncle Jim had set his heart on this family outing; and he was English, so nobody would be all that outraged.

Oma, who was very fond of Uncle Jim, said well, all right, but why Cleves? Why go all the way to Germany to enjoy ourselves? Weren't there cities every bit as pleasant and interesting inside Holland?

Tanta Marta, now very nettled indeed, said it had seemed to her nothing short of providential—the railway company choosing that very day to run an excursion. She then began to say something about travel broadening the mind, but spotting the smug look on our broadminded faces, promptly inquired if it wasn't time all these children were in bed.

So up to bed we had to go, with William grumbling away that somebody ought to mention to Tanta Marta that she wouldn't be having a silver wedding at all if it wasn't for our Uncle Jim.

Now the excursion train was due to leave Amsterdam at six sharp on the morning of the silver-wedding day. But we nine were up and washing at crack of dawn itself. Our Oma was going to show these Germans how a decent Dutch family turns out on such a day. Scrubbed and scoured the night before till we fairly shone, we had to undergo still more polishing and brushing before we finally passed muster. And Oma, very proud and satisfied, marched us off, each carrying a stiff little bouquet of flowers to offer, with our felicitations, to Tanta Marta.

As we hurried along the silent, empty streets, I thought how strange and unfriendly everything seemed—the shuttered shops and houses, the dark murmuring trees; as if they were very taken-aback and not at all pleased to see nine children and their Oma clattering along in their quiet secret dawn.

In Tanta Marta's flat, however, convivial pandemonium reigned, warm and free. Tanta Marta, hair beautifully waved, was bustling here, there, and everywhere, pouring

out coffee, and keeping an eagle eye on the packing of provisions merrily going on in the kitchen. Meanwhile, Uncle
Jim, wedged in a convenient corner behind the door,
offered sandwiches all round, and cigars to the gentlemen.
He also contrived to slip all nine of us a guilder each, with
a pleasing wink that clearly requested us to keep it dark.

At five-thirty sharp we set out for the station, laden with
baskets and hampers—snacks for the journey. It was billed
to take three hours, but Tanta Marta, to our whole-hearted
approval, was taking no chances.

And as we nine walked soberly along, we gave each
other little nudges, and exchanged significant nods. Oh yes!
We, too, had made our plans. We, too, were all set to
enjoy that silver wedding-day.

And the moment we arrived at the station, Jan gave a
loud whoop, and shot ahead, the rest of us close at his heels,
deaf to all shouts of protest echoing behind us. Through
the crowds we charged, and piled into one carriage of the
waiting train, four on one side, five on the other. And as we
had hoped and prayed, the grown-ups simply hadn't the
time to do anything about it, save hand us in our fair share
of the provisions, and hastily implore us not to hang our
heads from windows, open doors, throw out bottles or pull
the communication-cord, before they, too, had to join in
the scramble for seats.

Then off steamed the train, and our carriage set to work
to eat, drink, and make merry—without one thought, one
look at the beauty of the unfolding landscape. But by the
time the train drew up in Utrecht, all nine of us were hoarse,
but word-perfect in "Daisy, Daisy"; a Dutch ditty that
went, "Kling, klang, klock-a-by, sunshine makes me feel
so spry!", a German ballad about our hearts were like the

45

beehives, the maidens were the bees; and a lively French number that began, "I have lost the 'doh' of my clarinet."

And we had polished off every crumb, every drop of our share of the provisions.

So we took it in turns to hang out of the window to buy biscuits and chocolate. It was then that we spotted Uncle Jim, closely attended by the other gentlemen in the party, making their way across the crowded platform to the refreshment room.

Presently Mina, who was having her turn at the window, reported that Tanta Marta was now leaning out of *her* window, looking as cross as a spider.

Then the guard strolled by, and William, of course, began to wonder why Dutch guards didn't wave sensible flags, instead of waggling aloft a comic circle for all the world like a letter O on a stick.

But the sight of this guard must have been too much for Tanta Marta, for it was then that we heard her.

"J . . . im! Ji . . . im!"

Now, in all fairness to Tanta Marta, her voice was not loud and vulgar, but it *was* shrill and penetrating. People turned round. Heads shot out of windows.

"J-im! Ji-im!" called Tanta Marta, plainly very peeved. "J-im! J-IM!"

Suddenly, as if swept by lightning, the whole train took up the cry:

"Jim! Ji-im!"

Louder and merrier swelled the chorus.

"Jim! Ji-im!"

We looked at each other, dumb with dismay. That this should happen to *us*, to *our* family, and on a silver-wedding day, too!

But Jan jumped up, flung open the door of our carriage, and hared across to the refreshment room. And a moment later came out, followed by our errant uncle and company. And oh, as they swaggered along, they were all chanting too! " J-im! Ji-im!" they boomed as they covered the ground, and in the very nick of time, climbed back on our train. The door slammed behind them, and to a great gust of "J-im! Ji-im!" off we steamed.

And our carriage fell on Jan, and fondly thumped and pummelled him. This was more than one of his fine ideas, this was another victory, a glorious family victory!

Indeed, we were still rejoicing when the train slowed down at Arnhem. Instantly, doors flew open, heads appeared at every window, and up rose the cry again.

"J-im! Ji-im!"

Even the porters caught it. They obviously thought it must be the peculiar battle-cry of this particular excursion; and "J-im! Ji-im!" they bellowed as they clattered along in their clogs.

But more delightful still to us, we could hear Uncle Jim's great, deep voice roaring away with the best.

"J-im! Ji-im! Where the blazes is that Jim?"

And from then on, every time that train stopped, or slowed down, which it did with pleasing frequency, a thousand voices called for Jim, imploring him to return to his starving wife and twelve hungry children; to communicate with his loving mother who had made good the money he'd pinched from the bank; and other touching inventions.

And when at last we all spilled out on the station at Cleves, there was Tanta Marta, very pale and shaken, hanging on Uncle Jim's arm.

"Now," she began, striving to appear bright and unconcerned, "we must engage a reliable guide, and then . . ."

Uncle Jim patted her hand.

"Leave everything to Jim, my love," he said.

And from that moment on, our Uncle Jim took charge
of the day; and Tanta Marta, sincerely anxious to make
honourable amend, meekly fell in with his every suggestion.

Now I must be fair. If Tanta Marta had been in her usual,
efficient form, we would have combed Cleves from end to
end, seeing all the sights, missing nothing that the conscientious traveller ought to see. And all our memories
would have been orderly, accurate . . . and commonplace.

Whereas with Uncle Jim in charge, our progress through
Cleves was a regular, rip-roaring ride on the band-wagon,
for once he'd engaged a guide he hired five landaus for the
day. Yes, landaus! And blandly turning a deaf ear to all
warnings that we nine really ought to be split up safely
among the grown-ups, he packed us rejoicing into the last
landau.

I shall never forget it! We sat up with the driver and sang
orders to the horse. We sat on the hood. We sat on the
floor. We even at times sat on the seats. We sang, we waved,
we exchanged cordial battle-cries of "J-im! Ji-im!" with
humbler excursionists on foot. And every now and again
we'd hop out of our landau and kindly listen to the earnest
explanations of our guide—he was riding with Oma and
Uncle Jim and Tanta Marta in the first landau, of course.

Now this guide was a nice friendly young man from
Luxembourg who spoke every European language, *and*
understood American as well, or so he claimed. And after
the first couple of sights, he was Theodore to the lot of us,
and celebrating away, absolutely one of the family.

And Theodore knew his Cleves all right. We inspected simply everything, from the statue of Otto, the Cross Bowman, to the Castle and the Swan Tower. Our landau, I regret to say, laughed its head off at Theodore's romantic story about the knight of old who sailed up the river to Cleves in a beautiful little boat drawn by a lovely white swan. But we listened enthralled to his tale of an enterprising young woman who turned up one day in 1558, and said she was Anne of Cleves, back safe and sound from a prison in England. She indignantly said no, she certainly wasn't dead as everybody had supposed. Neither had she returned empty-handed. And swearing everybody to secrecy, she disclosed that she had managed to smuggle into her prison the Royal Crown of England, the Sceptre and the Orb, and twenty-five tons of solid gold. All of which she and another brawny young woman had let down on ropes from their prison window on the night they managed to escape, and every item of which they had carried back with them, all the way to Cleves.

And when Theodore said that the reigning Duke of Saxony actually fell for this convincing story, our Oma gave a significant "Och!" and marched triumphantly back to her landau. No Dutch duke, we felt, would have been taken in by *that* young woman.

But Oma's greatest moment was yet to come. An hour or so later, our landau decided it had seen enough churches, so we sat on outside the next one, whilst Theodore led our tireless relatives in to inspect it.

There we sat then, in the warm sunshine, speaking our minds about the ways of German sacristans who seemed to have a pay-before-you-look system all their own, and wave a large shopping-basket for tips under every visitor's nose, before they escort them to the next relic or tomb on the list.

Presently, down the street, came six or seven school-boys wearing peaked caps, and with long tin satchels on their backs. They stared at us, sitting up there in our landau, dressed in our Sunday best; and nudged each other.

"Cheese-heads!" they jeered. "Cheese-heads from Holland!"

Now a German thinks he is no end of a wag when he calls a Dutchman "Cheese-head". But the Dutch don't think much of the joke; and in return they call all Germans "Moffen".

I can't explain "Moffen", but it is an insult all right, and only used on Germans.

"Cheese-heads!" grinned the schoolboys again, very gratified at our frozen silence. "Fat young cheese-heads!"

That did it! Up from our landau we rose as one Dutch-man and with a mighty yell of "Moffen! Moffen!" we hurled ourselves upon them. And oh, it was Jan who led the attack, Jan who roared "Moffen!" loudest of all, as we fell on the foe.

But before we could really get going, the Moffen startled us by suddenly standing stiffly to attention. And there, note-book in hand, glaring down on us, towered a majestic policeman.

And there too, coming down the steps of the church, were our outraged relations.

In a split second, Oma sized up the scandal, and swiftly grabbing Theodore, she ordered him to translate her every word.

"This lady," said Theodore, "this gracious lady from Holland demands to know the reason of this unseemly

shindy, in front of a church, too, and in broad daylight!
The gracious lady demands to know where *you* were to
permit it. The gracious lady demands to know if she is to
inform the railway company, the newspapers, and your
burgomaster of the way your juveniles seize the opportunity
to insult decent Dutch tourists, with good money to spend
in your city."

All this the gracious lady demanded, and a great deal
more. And Theodore translated away with the utmost
pleasure. It was, so he told us later, a chance he had
almost prayed to have before he returned to his native
Luxembourg.

And before the policeman had time to open his mouth,
the gracious lady gave a final superb snort; majestically
waved us all back into our landaus; and off we drove.

And as our landau spanked round the corner, we gave a
rousing cheer to see the policeman whirl round, obviously
to cuff the young Moffen—all of whom we'd watched
silently disappearing as the gracious lady was speaking her
mind.

We had dinner that night in a restaurant near the station,
Theodore as well, of course. It was far more than an excellent meal, it was a triumph—for our Uncle Jim! The day
had gone beautifully to plan—his plan. Success soared to
his head; he cracked jokes; he sang songs; he made a first-
class speech. And Tanta Marta looked fondly on, even when
he set up a chorus that ran:

> *The man who shuns women, wine and song,*
> *Remains a fool his whole life long.*
> *So forget the missus! Forget all sorrow!*
> *Shall we be sensible? Yes, boys—to-morrow!*

But it was Oma, our Oma, who made the speech of the evening. She magnanimously conceded that perhaps a moral obligation did rest on the Dutch to travel abroad from time to time. To-day's experiences had proved that such travel was bound to have a civilising effect on other nations! And to roars of applause she sat down, and signalled to us.

One by one, we nine rose to our feet, stared at a spot high on a wall, and recited a verse each of a poem written by Oma's poor Olaf for another silver-wedding day—in days long past.

I had the last verse—a well-balanced mixture of sentiment and sound commonsense.

> *Hand and hand together,*
> *You have toiled the path of life*
> *You, beloved husband,*
> *You, devoted wife.*

I then went on to warn Uncle Jim and Tanta Marta that even now life wasn't going to be all blue skies and sunny hours; they must expect a few bracing showers. And I called down blessings rare on the happy pair; and hurriedly sat down.

And all the ladies wiped their eyes, and the gentlemen blew their noses, and Uncle Jim called for the bill, and we all set off for the station.

Theodore came to see us off; and he had drunk so many toasts to Uncle Jim and Tanta Marta that he didn't seem in the least astonished when the crowd on the station greeted us with a joyous roar of "J-im! Ji-im!"

In fact when the train drew out, he ran along the platform waving his straw hat, calling "J-im! Ji-im!" at the top of his voice—his last affectionate thank you for a very happy day—and a most generous tip.

And we nine hung out and waved and yelled too, till we could see him no more. Then we settled down to enjoy the journey home.

Suddenly, to everybody's surprise, Paul flung both arms about Jan.

"You were chic, chic!" he cried. "With those Moffen, I mean!"

Jan went very red.

"You also mean perhaps," he said stiffly, "that I am half Moffen, myself."

"Well, what about it?" said William.

"No. No!" protested Paul. "I only mean you are chic!" And he kissed Jan on both cheeks.

"Good—lord—good—night!" breathed William, plainly grateful that the chaps in Form 2B were not there to see these foreign cousins of ours.

"Come on!" said Jan, eyes very warm and bright. "Let's sing!"

And sing we did, all the way back to Amsterdam.

Chapter V

BAND OF HOPE

The next day we all began to pack to go home. And there was a certain comfort in the flurry and bustle of our hurried packing, for there was no time for thought or talk save on such urgent matters as where in Heaven's name was this and that and the other of our scattered belongings.

But I well remember how our Oma's face shone as we flung our arms about her that last evening, and thanked her for a holiday we would indeed remember all our lives long.

"My treasures!" said Oma. "My nine funny treasures!"

And we all laughed; but as she said it, why, suddenly, to my eyes she looked most beautiful. And I longed to say, "And we love you, too, Oma!"

But I didn't, of course. Nor did the others.

Looking back now, I can see, of course, that it was Jan, Jan as well as Oma, who made this holiday so outstanding.

There is no explaining it, but there are people who are born with a gift for the different, people who always seem up to the neck in something unusual, people to whom things *happen*. And our Cousin Jan was undoubtedly one of these people, Jan with his eternal, "Now, what have I for a fine idea!"

So you will understand our shrieks of joy when it was

decided the following spring, in a flurry of letters between my mother and Tanta Joh, that Jan was to come to England and stay with us for three months, and learn to speak good and fluent English. He already spoke fluent bad English.

He arrived on a Monday, and by the end of the week things were happening to us that had never happened before.

Our Wednesday evenings, for instance.

Now, before Jan came, our Wednesday evenings had been pleasant enough, but monotonous. Immediately after school, we would tear home for a meal, and then tear off again to call for Annie and Ricky Maloney. They were half Italian, half Irish, and their real names were Annunziata and Enrico, but we hadn't time for all that, of course.

They were the eldest of a family of seven, and they lived in a long narrow house with the whole length of the house running parallel to the pavement. This was most convenient, for we had only to turn the corner to hear if Mr. Maloney was at home and giving a music lesson—though "giving" is far too gentle a word for the manner of Mr. Maloney's tuition. He bellowed, he raved, he stamped up and down; indeed such was his artistic anguish that one felt, as one was meant to, that poor Mr. Maloney was forever doomed to cast pearls before the unteachable, cowering away in their parlour at three and six an hour.

Indeed, we once heard an interested listener on the pavement outside declare that it was a mercy for the backs and bellies of the young Maloneys that their Dad had his regular job in the orchestra down at the Theatre Royal, not to mention the business-like way he always screwed a quarter's fees in advance from every new and unsuspecting victim.

So when Mr. Maloney was at home, giving one of his lessons, we tiptoed round to their back door, and tapped cautiously till Ricky and Annie stole out to join us.

But if a loud rich clamour boiled briskly all over their house, with Mrs. Maloney arguing away in fine Italian style with all seven young Maloneys at once, then we knew it was safe to take it in turns to lean an elbow on their front-door bell, and beat spirited ra-ta-tats with their knocker, till the door flung violently open, and out fell Ricky and Annie.

But that was about all the excitement of our Wednesday evenings. We then had to trudge along three miles of dingy, twisting back-streets to our catechism class, where Father O'Leary stood no nonsense from any living child. We could, of course, have done the journey in half the time by keeping to the straight main-road, but that would have made things even duller and more monotonous.

The very first Wednesday we took Jan along, however, in came Father O'Leary's housekeeper and whispered in his ear.

" Is that so? " sighed Father O'Leary. "Bedlam! That's what this parish is fast becoming, and no mistake. Sure, the twelve apostles themselves wouldn't be one too many to cope with me troubles."

And he handed peppermints all round, told us to have the next six answers pat by next Wednesday or he'd have the skin off our backs, patted our heads, and sent us off, rejoicing. Never, never before had we had a whole shining Wednesday evening to squander just as we pleased.

But as we raced down the presbytery steps, Jan, as cool as you please, wheeled to the right.

"Wrong way!" we howled. "Come back! Wrong way!"

"Good!" cried Jan, and tore on. "We find something new!"

"But there's nothing there!" panted William. "Nothing there, I tell you."

But on and on raced Jan; and exasperated, protesting, we had to follow. Along one dismal road, round a corner, and into another.

"Told you so!" grunted William. "Wasting our time!"

But as we turned the next corner, there, spreading half across the road, pushing and shouting was a crowd of children, obviously waiting to go into a brightly-lit hall.

Jan's eyes sparkled.

"Vot dis?" he asked the nearest boy.

"Band of 'Ope," said the boy.

"Ah! Band of 'Ope," said Jan, as one who understood all.

"Penny a week, and a treat at Whitsun," went on the boy. Then noting the look on our penniless faces, added, "'S'all right. You needn't pay first time."

"Good!" approved Jan. "Very good!"

At that moment the doors opened, and with a mighty yell, the crowd surged forward. Immediately, Jan, waving and shouting with the rest, crashed ahead. And with a brilliant out-flanking movement, managed to secure seats in the very front row for all our party.

Breathless, excited, we gazed about us.

In front of us, on a platform, a tall thin young man was carefully pinning a large coloured picture on a blackboard. We stared and stared, and then recognised it with delicious horror. It was a picture of the human interior!

On the other side of the platform, a young lady in a smart pink silk blouse, was arranging sheets of music on a piano.

"Mama-mia!" sighed Annie Maloney. "Just like a real theatre!"

The next hour sped by like a beautiful dream. We sang strange hearty hymns with fine rollicking choruses. We listened with the greatest interest to the young man, who, armed with a long white pointer, showed us precisely what strong drink could do to the human interior. And to make things still more entrancing, we unanimously decided that the picture on the blackboard was the spit and image of Mr. Cousins, our Head Master; and followed his internal destruction with the utmost relish.

Then a short, stocky girl bounced out on the platform, holding a bunch of red paper roses, and gave us "Won't you buy my pretty flowers?" And we all joined in the chorus:

> *There are many sad and weary*
> *In this croo-ell world of ours,*
> *Singing every night so dreary,*
> *Won't you buy my pretty flowers.*

And I remember that the little girl hesitated for a moment before deciding on an encore, and some young wit in the back row bawled, "Go on, Maudie! Sing 'Down at the Old Bull and Bush'!"

This deplorable suggestion was, however, very coldly received by the young lady at the piano; so Maudie decided on a recitation, helped out with solemn chords, all about a poor little match-girl so ragged and thin whose saintly example saved both her back-sliding parents from that devil, called gin.

And I listened, almost in tears, wishing and wishing I had the luck to be an angelic match-girl too, when somebody gave me an impatient shove; and when I looked round, why, it was time to go home. And there was Jan,

busily explaining who we all were to the tall, thin young
man who was getting more and more muddled by our queer
assortment of foreign names. And Jan, ever obliging, was
offering to bring a piece of paper next week with all our
names on it, correctly spelt, when that noodle of a Ricky
Maloney suddenly put both his Italian feet in it. He said
he bet his Neapolitan mother wouldn't half have forty fits
to hear we'd been singing our drink was water bright,
because over there in Italy nobody ever dreamed of drinking
it. In fact they screamed blue murder if you tried it on. You
should have heard them one day when he'd tried to have
a drink of water . . . on the station at Milano it was. Perfect
strangers had bawled at him, and as for his mother, she had
boxed his ears, and carried on as if he'd been trying to
poison himself.

The young man, very shaken, said well, well, he never did.

But the young lady, shutting the piano, briskly said it was
a mercy we were all safe in England now, and no mistake.
And so goodbye now, till next Wednesday.

As we stepped out into the dark street, however, a sudden
chill snatched at our high spirits. How were we to explain
the Band of Hope, put it over at home, so that we could
count on a penny each every Wednesday, and the right to
stay out till half past eight?

Yes, how were we to achieve all that?

But we needn't have worried. Not with Cousin Jan about.

He marched us along in record time, grouped us artistically round the Maloney's front door, gave a gentlemanly
knock, and proceeded to interview Mrs. Maloney. And by
the time he had finished, it was crystal-clear that as sensibly
and naturally as night follows day, so a Band of Hope
should follow a Catechism Class.

Feeling much better, we then went on to tackle my mother. But here, we had one awful moment, for my mother, intrigued by the name, quite rightly demanded to know what we were being taught to hope for. And the feather-brained Annunziata promptly replied, "Oh, wine and gin and spirits and things!"

But Jan, giving her a dirty look, swiftly said in Dutch, "That dumb-head of an Italian never listens to anything!" and adroitly went on to lay great stress on the cultural side of the Band of Hope, saying how much, for instance, they'd all enjoy hearing our William recite one Wednesday. William gave a yelp of dismay; but my mother, quite won over, said yes, that would be nice, and that William could wear his nice new suit and recite his nice new poem about the sailor-boy.

And sure enough, a fortnight later, buttoned into an imaginative Dutch tailor's idea of an American sailor-suit, our William flew on the platform, glowered at the waiting Band of Hope, and gabbled:

> *I am a little sailor-boy,*
> *And would you know my story?*
> *I've sailed across the ocean blue,*
> *And known it in its glory.*

There were six other nautical verses, all of which William delivered at such a speed that the Band of Hope kindly decided he must be reciting in Dutch. And when he came to a breathless halt, they politely waited for the rest—in silence. Not a clap from anybody.

William glared; waited, and then indignantly began to clap himself, looking so ferocious that even the tall, thin young man doubled up in a great guffaw. And the young lady was heard to declare that boy was a card, and no mistake.

But it was Jan, of course, Jan, who took the Band of Hope by storm. He, if you please, volunteered to do a Conjuring Act!

Now conjurors in our simple day were dazzling beings who only walked our earth on rare occasions. So, buzzing with excitement one Wednesday night, the Band of Hope watched our Cousin Jan walk on the platform carrying a large canvas valise he had borrowed from my mother. Even we had no idea what was in it. Waving graciously, Jan then disappeared behind the piano.

Three minutes later, a joyous roar tore up. Jan was waddling out from behind the piano, and now he bulged everywhere, simply everywhere—before, behind, and on both sides. Even his sleeves and stockings stuck out like crooked half-moons.

Then Jan clicked his heels, bowed, and waved for silence. And with a magnificent gesture he spread wide an empty hand, plunged it inside his shirt-front, and produced in quick succession: a book, a doll, two knives and forks, a ball of string, and a small tin saucepan. All of which he flourished aloft for us to see as if he had spirited them there from the thinnest of air.

From his stockings he then whipped out a tea-pot, two cups and saucers, and a small loaf of bread.

From his sleeves he pulled a brush and comb, a feather duster, six stiff white collars, a mouth-organ and a rolling-pin.

Then came the Grand Finale.

He picked up the mouth-organ, dusted it with the feather-duster, and began to play a catchy little German number:

Band of Hope

Oh, you darling Augustine, Augustine, Augustine,
Oh, you darling Augustine,
Everything's gone!
Cash is gone, girl is gone,
Everything's gone.

And turning his back on us, he undid the two back buttons of his braces; and with a truly Continental disregard for the "nice", he plunged his free hand into the seat of his pants, gave a dramatic heave, and began to pull out yard upon yard of thin white paper.

The Band of Hope gaped. Then gave an almighty roar. And Jan, still playing away, unrolled and unrolled, his posterior shrinking before our rapturous eyes, as wave after wave of toilet-paper piled higher and higher on the platform.

At one moment it looked as if the scandalised young man was about to advance on him. But such a yell of protest tore up from the ranks, that he hastily retreated; and very disapproving, watched our indelicate cousin, reduced now to normal, bowing to right and to left, and blowing the most foreign of kisses to the delirious Band of Hope.

"Good old Fritzie!" they yelled. "Good old German sausage!"

And "good old German sausage" he was to them all from that triumph on.

They honoured him even more. When Whit Monday came, all the Bands of Hope in our district marched to a combined treat—sports, prizes, and tea, in a field two good miles outside the town.

A brass band led the procession, playing every step of the way. Behind them marched William and Ricky and many another well-scrubbed boy, each carrying a cane on which was tied a large bow of blue ribbon.

Then came two great cart-horses, brasses shining like gold, pulling along a lorry on which our Band of Hope had staged a most grim and squalid tableau: The Drunkard's Home.

And our popular, our lucky cousin had been unanimously elected to be the star of that tableau! Yes, there he rode, up on that lorry, fairly wringing the hearts of all the spectators—by far the most piteous of all the Drunkard's destitute children.

And I remember that it was a beautiful day, very sunny and warm, and that we girls, in white dresses, walked behind The Drunkard's Home, chattering like sparrows.

And Maudie told me that her Dad had told her Mum that he knew for a fact that all the public-houses on our route had lain in extra barrels of beer to cope with the thirst of the spectators lining the streets to cheer us on our way.

But this didn't strike me as in the least odd. On the contrary, I thought it was a most sympathetic gesture, quite a compliment to our Band of Hope, in fact.

Chapter VI

SUNDAY AFTERNOON

Maybe I ought to admit now that our Cousin Jan wasn't nearly so popular with the grown-ups of the family as he was with us. Our Dutch Uncle Henk, for instance, often darkly remarked, "That boy has too easy a tongue. Take care he doesn't grow up a liar."

Nobody took this very seriously, however. We all knew that our Uncle Henk had been brought up in a remote and fiercely Calvinistic village in Friesland where conversation was a sober exchange of facts, and no time-wasting discussions encouraged, except, of course, on such accredited Dutch arguments as: Did the Snake really speak?

But I can see now that Uncle Henk undoubtedly had some cause for alarm. Our Cousin Jan certainly had a way of improving on the truth. If a story was dull, he simply couldn't resist polishing it up a little. If current events were flat and tedious, he freely translated them into something worth the telling.

We listened to him, entranced. We knew he was making half of it up, of course, but that didn't matter. Any poor wit can trump up a yarn when driven to it. Whereas our Cousin Jan told tall stories because he enjoyed the exercise. And that makes all the difference to any entertainment.

There was one Sunday afternoon in particular that I shall never forget.

After Sunday School, we were supposed to go for a good brisk walk. Our Dutch mother had not yet got round to the British ritual of afternoon tea, and we still had a solid meal about half-past six every evening, a combined tea and supper as it were. So there was always ample time for our nice, long Sunday walk.

But instead of stepping it out along the green country lanes, as I suppose our parents fondly imagined we did, we had our own secret beat through a dense tangle of mean little streets till we came to a dingy shop, open on Sundays, and which sold home-made fig-toffee—stout enduring stuff that stuck round our teeth, chewable for hours on end, and four ounces a penny.

From there, we always made for a large public-house, called "The Garrick", which displayed bills for the nearby Theatre Royal, handsome pictorial bills, which we examined minutely every Sunday.

One Sunday it would be two little sailor-boys struggling valiantly with a masked villain in faultless evening-dress, who was trying to push them both off a high bridge into the foaming river below.

Another Sunday it would be "The Girl who took the Wrong Turning" in a rich scarlet satin gown, and obviously celebrating it by knocking back a large goblet of sparkling ruby-red wine.

But on this particular Sunday it was a picture of a sad lady dressed in black from head to toe, sitting in a black velvet armchair, weeping over a large photograph of an angelic little boy. And in a balloon floating over her head, it said:

"And he never called her 'Mother'!"

William, who liked his facts plain, immediately asked, "Well, what did he call her then?" And still speculating on this, and chewing our toffee, we drifted on till we came to a smart new chapel with two doors in its wide front porch. As we passed by, these doors opened wide, and two gentlemen, one short, one tall, took up their posts, one at each door. And we were deeply interested to observe that as the congregation filed out, everybody paused for a moment to shake hands with one or the other of the two smiling gentlemen.

"Now!" muttered Jan. "What have I for a fine idea! Come! Come, quick!"

He made for the side of the chapel. There was a door there, too. He cautiously tried it. It opened willingly; and in we went.

A minute later we too were shaking hands with the tall gentleman.

Two minutes later we were shaking hands with the short gentleman.

And then with the tall gentleman.

And again with the short gentleman.

It was wonderful! So wonderful that we failed to notice the stream of traffic was growing thinner and thinner. And the next time we filed past the tall gentleman, the pleasant smile froze on his face. He looked at Jan . . . that queer German jacket . . . that comic German hair-cut . . .

"Here, you!" he demanded. "What's the little game? Round and round the mulberry bush, eh?"

"Mulberry bush?" echoed Jan. "No speak much English, sir! You shake hands, please? Please shake, sir!"

And he held out his hand with such a winning smile that the gentleman obliged; and, rooted to the spot, watched us march sedately off.

"Foreigners!" he explained compassionately to the gentleman at the other door.

Once round the corner, the leader of the foreigners burst into a wild can-can.

"I won!" he crowed. "Five times I shaked! I am champion, champion of the shake-hand!"

He broke off, and grinned at a little girl who was watching him with round, solemn eyes, a little girl carrying a jam-pot and a tight bunch of flowers.

"What you do with those?" he asked.

"Going to put 'em on Gran's grave," said the little girl.

"Good, kind little girl!" approved Jan. "We come with you. Yes, we come, too!"

So we all went to the cemetery.

And on the way, the little girl told us about her Gran's funeral. The insurance money simply hadn't covered it. Mum was like that, everything of the best. Gran, censorious in life, just couldn't have wished for a finer send-off: lovely wreaths with purple bows on them, and three sittings to tea in the parlour afterwards: ham, tongue, cucumber, and sponge fingers.

Deeply impressed, we then helped the little girl to fill her jam-pot at a tap just inside the gate of the cemetery, and looked around us in awed interest. It was about five o'clock now, tea-time for everybody in Great Britain except us and this dutiful little girl. We had that great solemn cemetery to ourselves. No other living soul anywhere.

"Ach!" said Jan sadly. "It is NOT beautiful. Now in Antwerp . . ."

"Yes, yes, I swear I have been to Antwerp. I tell you, I *have* been there! With my mother, to meet my father, I went. And in Antwerp there is a beautiful cemetery, flowers all over everywhere!"

"Plenty here, too," said William. "Bit patchy, that's all."

"Ach!" sighed Jan. "And how do they feel, those poor deads, looking down and seeing not one flower for them? How do they feel?"

We looked at each other in awkward silence. That was the worst of these foreign relations of ours, the way they *would* talk about things, never mind how uncomfortable.

"Well, we can't help it," began my sister truculently.

"No? No?" queried Jan. "Listen!"

And long before our golden-tongued cousin paused to take breath, we knew where our bounden duty lay. We knew we must, in all charity, take upon ourselves the more equitable distribution of all these wreaths and flowers.

Solemnly, silently, we set to work.

" 'Ere!" gasped the little girl, very alarmed. "You won't 'alf cop it, carting all them wreaths about!"

We explained our high purpose. The little girl said we'd cop it all the same, and that she wasn't going to be mixed up in it, she wasn't. She was going home to tea, she was.

Half an hour later we felt we had better go home as well. We were beginning to feel very hungry. More urgent still, a thin trickle of visitors was now coming through the cemetery gates, and we knew better than to wait on gratitude from any living adult.

As we plodded home, my sister suddenly lifted up her voice, and sang.

"Ring the bells of Heaven!" she carolled. "There is joy to-day."

"You think so?" said Jan, very wistful and melancholy. "Me . . . I am asking myself . . ."

We stared at him in tired dismay. Now what was he asking himself?

"We'll go on with it, of course," said William crossly. "We'll go on every Sunday till they've all got a share."

"Of course!" said Jan, sternly. "But it is not enough. I am thinking that in Antwerp they also have beautiful wreaths made of coloured beads with china birds on them; and hanging on the . . . the . . . yes, the tombstones, there are photographs, fine photographs in frames."

This was too much!

"Liar!" we said. "Liar!"

Jan danced up and down on the pavement. He swore he was telling the truth. He conceded, under pressure, that maybe he had exaggerated a little about swimming across the River Rhine smoking a cigar; but this, this, so help him, this was true! TRUE. There *were* photographs! With his own two eyes, he had seen them! Oh, all right, maybe not on every tombstone, but on most of them. And it was a good idea, a fine idea. You weren't scared any more when you saw how *they* looked—smiling, cheerful, and in their best clothes.

Now, if we could . . .

"We can't!" said William, flatly. "We just can't. Nobody would give us their photographs."

"But, listen!" cried my sister, eyes shining like stars. "We could give them nice pictures—what we think they must have looked like."

"Pictures!" hooted William. "Where would we get them?"

"Magazines," said my sister.

"Now!" approved Jan. "Now! What is that for a fine idea!"

All the following week we toiled like beavers. We found old copies of Dutch and English magazines—I remember one was called Knitted Garments for Gentlemen; and we borrowed scissors right and left, and worked and worked.

Nobody inquired what we were up to. In our happy-go-lucky home children could be heard and seen all over the place. More comfortable still, we knew nobody would ever dream of stopping what they were doing to ask awkward questions or even to watch and listen. So as we cut and clipped, we discussed and argued endlessly. We had set ourselves the very highest standards; only the handsomest pictures would do.

And this I will swear to: we were in deadly earnest. Our hearts shone within us. We felt reverently, tenderly benevolent. We moved most solemnly and earnestly in a high celestial world to which we alone held the key.

And when Saturday came, we sorted all our pictures into six comprehensive groups: Ladies—old, young. Gentlemen —old, young. Children—boys, girls.

Then we spent every penny of our week's pocket money on crayons, and lovingly coloured in every picture.

And we went one better than Antwerp. We bestowed a yellow halo and a pair of pale-blue wings on each of the Chosen.

On Sunday afternoon we carefully wrapped them all in tissue paper, packed them in my new school-satchel, and set off for Sunday School.

And Father O'Leary, I remember, was downright worried at the sight of our solemn faces, not to mention our absent-minded replies to his questions, especially when William advanced the theory that Matrimony was an outward sign of inward grace.

"Is it sickening for something ye are?" he asked. And sent us off early, just in case.

But the moment we walked through the cemetery gate, a red-faced man pounced savagely upon us.

He demanded to know who we were, and what we thought we were up to. Without waiting to hear, he said he knew us all right. We were the four young devils who'd been messing about with other people's flowers last Sunday. He said the POLICE were after us. He said people were writing to the PAPERS about us. He said kids like us ought to be smothered at birth, playing about in cemeteries when decent Christians were sitting down to their Sunday teas. Except him, of course. He wasn't expected to have *his* tea in peace, *he* wasn't! Eyes in the blasted back of his head, he was supposed to have, he was.

He then gave awful details of what would happen if we ever dared to show our nasty faces inside his cemetery again. And still storming away, he stood like the Avenging Angel in the gateway, and watched our silent retreat.

Nobody spoke. Not even Jan. We walked along in grey desolation. Just walked.

Presently I stopped, opened my satchel, and took out the pictures. And saw them through a mist.

"Oh, tear them up!" said William, and walked ahead with my sister.

Jan remained at my side.

"People!" he gulped. "People are . . . terrible."

And he wept too, as the wind scattered all our celestial hierarchy along the dingy street.

Chapter VII

OMA'S LETTERS

A fortnight later Jan went back to Germany, and never shall I forget the look on his face when we arrived at the station and my mother made him put on his overcoat. For there, neatly tacked on the lapel was a white linen label with his name and destination printed on it in large red capital letters. More mortifying still, my mother had a long and earnest conversation with the guard, and we could hear him promising to hand our Cousin Jan over, with a five-shilling tip, to the steward on board the steamer to Hamburg, where his father would be waiting to collect him.

"Just as if he were a parcel, or deaf and dumb or something," sympathised William.

Nor did it make things better when we heard my mother half-apologising for this unusual fussing.

"He's an only child, you see!"

But Jan's face lit up again as the train began to draw out, and we three pulled out our whistles and blew a long, fond blast of farewell. And Jan, hanging half out of the window, deaf to all my mother's last-minute injunctions, shouted, "Till next year, then! Till next year!" And pulled out his whistle, and blew and blew.

But there was to be no next year, for this was May, 1914. And we woke up one sunny August morning to hear my mother crying, "Not war! Oh, not war!"

And my father's care-free voice, "Don't worry! It will be over by Christmas!"

But that Christmas came and heavily went, and by the time the next Christmas came round, Jan's father, our Uncle Gottlieb, was in the German Navy; our own father was in the British Expeditionary Forces; and our Uncle Piet, now a naturalised Frenchman, was in the French Army.

And all through those long, nightmare years, our Oma in Amsterdam prayed for us all; knitted countless warm socks for the International Red Cross with strict instructions to hand them out to Allied and German prisoners-of war alike; and every evening rain or shine sat down to write her letters.

Oma's letters. I still have a bundle of the ones she sent to my mother. I have them here on the desk as I write. And as I read them I can hear her kind, homely voice, filled now with pain and bewilderment.

Dear Anna,

With deepest sorrow I take up my pen to write you that yesterday I received from Joh the sad news that our beloved Gottlieb was reported missing, feared drowned. And that this is now officially confirmed.

Anna, I cannot tell you the grief this war brings to me. Every day when I dust that last holiday photograph we had taken in Cleves, I look at Gottlieb, arm in arm with your husband and Piet, so friendly and merry. And I ask myself, how can it be right that such men must now fight each other in a war?

Anna, Joh does not write more except to say she and Jan are well, and that he is growing very tall.

But I am anxious about him. Now is he fatherless, and this is bad for a boy. Then a growing boy needs much good food, and we read in our papers that there is great hunger in Germany. I send a parcel every week, but they do not always receive them.

Anna, I will write more next week. To-day my heart is too full.

And this wasn't the only time that Oma took up her pen to write in bitterness and grief.

"Do not believe, dear Anna, that over here in Holland we are all making money from the misery of this war. It is not true. I tell you that it is the few, the wretched few who are making fortunes—just as in other lands so I am told. Believe me, the many others of us pray for peace and do all we can to help. And to tell the truth, here, too, there is much hardship. So little coal that many factories have been obliged to close down, and tens of thousands are out of work. Here in Amsterdam alone, one out of every two has no job and must live on charity. And this, when prices are rising and rising.

"Anna, we must all pray for peace. Blows never solved any problems, in families or in nations."

Then in many of her letters Oma wrote of a boy called Pierre, a refugee from Brussels whom she took into her home and cared for as if he were her own grandson.

"The poor boy does not know what happened to his family, but it is feared they are all dead. He was in a sad state when he first arrived, but he is beginning to look better now. And now I have him here, I feel better, too. It is always good to have someone to look after. He reminds me of Paul and Philippe. Such dark eyes."

We three in England often talked about this Belgian boy, wondered what he was like, and whether he had come across the first-class pea-shooter which William had accidentally left behind, stuck in the sand of one of Oma's ornaments—Oma always filled her ornaments with sand so that they wouldn't topple over easily. And one day William said he wished Oma would tell us if Pierre had found it, or something else really interesting about the chap, instead of just writing he was well, or had a cold in his head, and stuff like that. And my sister and I were agreeing when, to our surprise, our easy-going mother fairly exploded. She said this was too much, coming from three lazy, ungrateful youngsters who had never written a letter yet of their own free will in all their lives; and even those we had to be coerced into writing all began: Thank you for my nice present.

And my mother, fiercely wiping up the dishes and mopping her eyes, said she could only hope against hope that one day we would improve, then maybe we would have the sense to recognise a beautiful, unselfish letter when we read one.

We listened in silence. We had at least learned to recognise the truth when we heard it.

In March, 1918, Oma wrote her shortest, saddest letter. Her only son, our Uncle Piet, and his French wife, Yvonne, were both dead.

Uncle Piet had gone to Paris on an unexpected twenty-four hour leave. He wired Tante Von-von, and she had rushed there to join him, leaving our cousins, Paul and Philippe, with their grandparents in Marseilles.

That week-end the German High Command decided to try out their new long-distance weapon: an enormous cannon, trained on Paris.

At three o'clock that Good Friday afternoon, Uncle Piet and his wife knelt in prayer in the crowded church of Saint

Gervais. A moment later they lay dead, buried under the ruins.

Oma, it seems, wrote many letters to Marseilles, first suggesting, then almost pleading to be given the charge of Paul and Philippe—"the children of my only son".

Pinned on one of Oma's letters I found this reply. Oma must have sent it on for my mother to read.

Dear Madame and Friend,

We have safely received your letter of Monday last, and again we must thank you for all your kindness.

Dear Madame, we have never met you, but Piet and Von-von so often talked about you, and always with so much affection, that we feel we know you quite well.

We will, therefore, open our hearts to you with utmost frankness.

First, you must believe that your dear son Piet was also a son to us—so good and kind a husband to our beloved daughter. But now they are both dead. And we must decide what is to become of their children.

Dear Madame, forgive us if we point out that you have other children. Now, we have none.

You have other grandchildren. We have only Paul and Philippe.

Believe us, we understand so well how dearly you would like them to come to you in Amsterdam. But do not ask this of us. We beg you not to ask it.

They shall write regularly to you. We will send photographs. When times are better, they will visit you.

With this, we send a copy of Piet's last photograph in his uniform of Maréchal des Logis.

Affectionate kisses from the boys, and please accept, dear Madame, the assurance of our affectionate esteem.

MARIE AND MARIUS DUPONT

So Paul and Philippe remained in Marseilles with their French grandparents; and Oma wrote to them every Sunday, just as on Tuesdays she wrote to us in England, and on Thursdays she wrote to Tanta Joh and Jan in Germany, linking us all together in a chain of homely, loving letters.

Dear Oma! So anxious, so determined that her scattered family at least should have the sense to remain friends in that torn and quarrelling world.

All this while, of course, we nine grandchildren were fast growing up. And I came home one day to find my mother busily unpicking the hem of William's winter overcoat, when to my dismay, she suddenly burst into tears.

"If this goes on," she wept, "he won't need it. He will be in uniform. And so will Jan. Sisters' sons training to kill each other!"

But this was spared us. The war came to an end.

But Oma's worries were not at an end; for now, week after week, there was no news from Tanta Joh and Jan. And there were grim headlines in all the Dutch newspapers:

Starvation in Germany! Chaos!

Then Oma had become very attached to Pierre, the boy from Brussels; but now an uncle and aunt turned up to claim him; and he went back with them to Belgium.

I found a beautifully written letter from him amongst Oma's old papers. He was obviously thanking her for a book she had sent him for his birthday, but it was the last part of his letter that I found so moving:

There was such a bad feeling in me when I left you, Oma. But now you write to me every Saturday, I feel like those others to whom you write every week. I kiss you, dear Oma, as I love you, with all my heart.

Your Belgian Boy,

PIERRE.

Yes, Pierre from Brussels was also on our Oma's letter-list, another link in her dear, homely chain of love.

Now many a cruel and ill-informed thing was said and written in those days about Holland and her determination to keep out of that war.

But very little was ever written or said about one thing— Dutch kindness to children both during and after the war, and never mind what nationality. No, little or nothing was ever known outside Holland of the way the Dutch flung open their frontiers, and into thousands and thousands of Dutch homes poured the children, first from Belgium, and then from Germany and Austria.

And our Dutch grandmother worked every free hour in one of the rest-centres for these children; and I have been told that as she encouraged them to eat, and poured out their milk, she would often say to an older child, "Tell me, my treasure, back there in Germany did you ever come across a tall boy called Jan, Jan Bauer? Oh, he'd be older than you, of course; he was seventeen last April."

But not a child had ever met our Cousin Jan.

And Oma's heart grew heavier and heavier for each batch of children now coming from Germany seemed more peaked, more listless, more half-starved than the last.

Then one Sunday—and oh, the times I have heard her re-live it!—Oma got up very early, Heaven above only knew why, she wasn't wanted down at the rest-centre that day. And she sat down to her solitary breakfast—she still lived alone in the rooms above the shop, stoutly refusing to go and live with Tanta Mina and Uncle Henk in their smart modern flat in the south of Amsterdam, declaring she was too bossy a body to share a flat with any woman, least of all her own daughter.

Well, there sat our Oma then, having her breakfast, when for no reason at all, she pushed back her plate and a great lump came up in her throat. And for two pins, the tears would have rolled down her face as she thought, "Now, what is this for a fine world! All this quarrelling and fighting and hating!"

Then she sharply told herself she wasn't precisely helping Providence to improve matters—just sitting there, grizzling.

So she set to work to clear the table, and dust and tidy her spotless living-room. And she watered all her plants and sponged their leaves—she dearly loved a handsome plant. Then she looked about her, hesitated for a moment, slipped off her apron, pulled on her shopping-coat, and set off to do something she had never done before—not on a Sunday! Never, never on a Sunday!

She went to the flower-shop at the end of the road. And Mevrouw van der Berg was just about to draw the blinds and lock up the till, when she saw our Oma walk in. And as she herself told me, she was so surprised, her mouth seemed full of teeth, for she knew Oma's rigid views on Sunday trading.

And Oma chose a fine bunch of tall yellow daisies, to be paid for first thing on Monday; and hurried back with them hoping the neighbours were not at their windows. And she tipped out all the sand from the big blue Delft jug that she always kept on her old-fashioned writing-desk between her illustrated Bible and the poems of Jacob Catz; and she arranged the daisies in it; and then stood back to admire them.

"Now!" she said to herself. "What am I for an old fool, feeling this way, as if I were expecting company!"

But there was no stifling that strange feeling. So she set to work to bake a great apple-tart, a thing she had not done since Pierre had gone, saying to herself she would take it down to the rest-centre for the children's supper that evening.

As she was putting it in the oven, the door-bell rang. So she went to the top of the stairs and pulled the rope that opened the street-door downstairs.

"Come up, Corrie!" called Oma, thinking it was her old friend, Mevrouw Kamp, who always looked in for a chat about this time of a Sunday. And she hurried back to the kitchen to get out the coffee-pot.

Feet came up the stairs, and Oma cried, "You'll have a cup of coffee with me, of course?"

"Ja, ja . . . Oma!"

Oma spun round. The cup she held in her hand fell, and crashed on the tiled floor.

There stood a gaunt woman, the tears streaming down her tired face. And there beside her, clutching a large canvas bag, stood a tall, thin lad.

"Now!" whispered Oma. "Now may our dear Lord be thanked."

And then they were in her arms.

They were home. Tanta Joh and Jan were home, home with Oma.

Chapter VIII

CRAB-APPLE TREE

Nobody ever learned much of what happened to Tanta Joh and Jan during those black desolate war-years, for the simple reason that they both hated talking about them.

But from Oma we heard that they had spent the last months of the war with Jan's German grandmother who lived in a quiet little town in Bavaria. Tanta Joh had often sent us brightly coloured picture-postcards from there in the days before the war, and from time to time Jan had told us some entrancing details about his German Oma—at least I thought they were entrancing.

We knew, for instance, that she lived in a little red-brick villa that looked for all the world like an outsize dolls' house, with two cherry-trees in the front garden and five in the back. And everything inside her house was very neat and clean and smelt of furniture polish, and in the living-room there was a wonderful stove built of coloured tiles; and on the wall over this stove hung the pipe his German grandfather used to smoke—a beautiful pipe with red tassels hanging from its carved stem, and a large china bowl with a lid on it which had to be lifted up every time his grandfather filled his pipe with tobacco.

And his German Oma always embroidered red and blue flowers on the tops of all her sheets; and the only time she got really mad was when Jan absent-mindedly crumpled her stiff white muslin curtains.

And every Sunday she used to make a delicious kind of apple-cake, and very special coffee with whipped cream piled high on every cup, as rich as any you could drink in Vienna where his German Oma had once spent a holiday.

I loved to think about all this, especially at Christmas-time when Jan's German grandmother always sent us a card. To my mind it was the very loveliest of all our Christmas cards for we had only to pull a little flap, and her card would open out and up into Bethlehem itself, with little German angels everywhere, very rosy and merry, briskly playing strange celestial instruments to a jocund Child with fair curly hair and bright blue eyes.

All this made me feel that Jan's Oma must surely live in a beautiful fairy-tale sort of place where everything was brightly coloured and very cheerful. But when I once asked Jan what it was like, he said it wasn't at all the place *he* would like to live in, far too many old ladies eternally invit-ing each other to coffee-parties with the most important lady sitting in state on the sofa, and all of them expecting a boy to enjoy himself in a corner, absolutely dumb except when spoken to, even when handing round the cakes.

Then, sensing my disappointment, he hastily added that it was quite all right for a holiday if one had a bicycle, and there really was something very nice about his Oma and her house. "Gemütlich," people used to say. He couldn't translate it. So we looked it up in the dictionary: good-natured, genial, kindly-disposed, cosy, snug. And Jan said yes, it was a mixture of all that, most of the time; but not, oh not when there was a coffee-party on.

Nothing in the little town, however, was in the least

cosy and snug during the last few months of that First World War. Something went wrong with the drains, something that needed men and money to put right. The Corporation had neither. Indeed, Tanta Joh told Oma that there wasn't an able-bodied man left in the place. She said everybody did what they could, but it wasn't enough. And all that hot summer long, there was case after case of dysentery and typhoid. And though Tanta Joh boiled every drop of water they used, on the first Monday of September, Jan's grandmother was taken very ill and was rushed off to the crowded little hospital.

On the Wednesday, something made her lift her poor old head from her pillow—to see Tanta Joh being carried in on a stretcher.

"Du lieber Gott!" she prayed, and closed her tired eyes; and died.

Three days later Jan was carried off to the hospital of a neighbouring town. And Tanta Joh lay in her bed, too numb and exhausted to worry, which was perhaps as well, for outside the hospital walls there were hunger, despair and ever-growing chaos.

But the moment Tanta Joh could sit up and hold a pen, she had written to our Oma in Amsterdam. So, it seemed, had Jan. But what happened to their letters, nobody knew. Burnt maybe, that being quicker and cheaper than baking them or whatever it was the harassed, overworked staff were supposed to do to prevent the epidemic from spreading.

Then, when Tanta Joh crawled at last out of hospital, it was to find the red-brick villa occupied by three tight-lipped, elderly aunts from Cologne, who lost no time but straightway produced legal documents which proved that the villa and all its contents had passed to them to enjoy for life. And it was no use criticising them, for they, too, were well-nigh demented. All their hard-earned savings were now practically worthless; and day by day the prices were soaring and soaring.

Now a woman in the hospital bed next to Tanta Joh's had confided in her that her husband occasionally took a lorry into Holland on some peculiar business of his own. And to cut a long story short, this man agreed to take Tanta Joh and Jan with him on his next trip—at a price. But there was one costly delay after another. The little money they still had melted away, even though they were now making do with one meal a day—two slices of bread spread with mashed potato for Jan, one slice for Tanta Joh.

And then . . .

But Oma said that, at this point of their story, Tanta Joh cried oh, what did it matter? What did anything matter now they were safe again, safe in Holland with Oma.

And Jan, it seemed, sniffed the air, his eyes sharp and bright in his peaked face.

"Oma," he said, "do I smell Heaven?"

And Oma gave a shriek and flew to her oven. And when she opened the door, there was her apple tart, golden-brown, done to a turn.

We had a very long letter from Oma telling us all this, but it was the last part of Oma's letter that was to haunt me so for many, many a night.

She wrote that Tanta Joh and Jan arrived home not an hour too soon. Early that Sunday afternoon, a low suffo-cating blanket of fog came rolling in from the sea towards Amsterdam. By late evening it had swallowed up every street, every bridge. By nightfall every familiar sleepy

gracht had become a sinister death-trap; and in spite of the
lamps, the fires burning in braziers all along the banks,
thirteen poor souls walked to their deaths that night in the
dark, waiting water.

And among them was one of Oma's friendliest neighbours—plump, jolly Mevrouw Vos. She left four children,
all boys; and as Oma wrote, her husband, a quiet, retiring
soul who always left everything to his capable wife. And
all because young Kees had slipped out to gallop round in
that strange, exciting fog; and his mother, still in her apron,
had gone hurrying after him to bring him back.

And I lay awake at night, not thinking of Tanta Joh
and Jan—they were safe now with Oma; but seeing poor
Kees Vos turning up safe and sound, and very pleased with
his adventure . . . till he saw his father's face.

To everyone's relief, Tanta Joh and Jan settled down
very comfortably with Oma. Tanta Joh lent a hand in the
shop, and Jan found a promising job with an important
shipping company.

But Jan's promising job didn't last long. Without saying
a word to anyone, he handed in his notice, and found himself
another job, in the office of a coffee-importer this time. But
coffee didn't seem to interest him long, either; and when
next we heard from Oma, he was handing out leaflets and
information from behind the counter of a travel-agency.

Presently Oma's letters began to hint that it wasn't only
the way Jan changed jobs that was so disturbing, there was
also the question now of his military service. The head-
strong lad, if we pleased, was coolly refusing to consider
going into the Dutch army for this. Oh, not because it was
Dutch, but because it was an army. He argued there was

no more need for armies, not after this war to end all wars. So he wasn't going to waste precious time marching and square-bashing in any language. And he came home one evening, and announced that he had claimed exemption on the ground that his father had been German. So there he was now, forever inscribed and classified in official records as: German by birth. Born in Hamburg.

"What is done," wrote Oma, "cannot be undone. The real trouble is that even now he simply cannot seem to settle down. At first he is full of enthusiasm for every new job; then home he walks, and casually mentions between two mouthfuls of supper that he has again handed in his notice, that again he has something more interesting in view.

"I tell Joh not to worry. Jan is a good boy at heart, and many a young man settles down all the better once he has discovered life cannot be all change and excitement. But this lesson, of course, each of us must learn for himself."

Oma, however, must also have had her misgivings, for one evening, when she was alone with Jan, it seems she ordered him into the parlour, and told him to sit down on the sofa as if he were a three-year-old.

Then she put on her spectacles, unlocked her writing-desk, and took out a yellow roll of paper, tied with a faded blue ribbon.

"Jan," said Oma, unrolling the paper. "I think it is high time I read you a poem written by your grandfather. In my opinion it is the best my poor Olaf ever wrote."

And she gave a solemn little cough, and began to read our grandfather's poem.

To Jan's surprise, it was most romantic, all about a fair maiden of Ancient Greece, called Corinna, to whom the capricious gods on High Olympus gave the chance of a life-time.

At crack of dawn one golden day they set Corinna down in their celestial orchard, free as air, to make her choice. Yes, all that Corinna had to do was halt before any fine tree she fancied, and it would be hers, to blossom and fruit eternally. There was one small condition however—Corinna had but one day; she had to make up her mind before nightfall.

But when one is young and happy, sang poor Olaf, a day is packed with shining hours; so, on and on, wandered fair Corinna, bare feet dancing over the soft, green grass, singing for dear delight in all that scented loveliness. Carefree, unheeding, on, on, she danced.

And only when the first pale star shone out in the darkening sky, did she give a little sigh.

"This will do," she said, and sank down at the foot of the nearest tree.

But when she looked up, ah me, she had chosen a crab-apple tree!

"A crab-apple tree," repeated Oma, and looked at Jan over the top of her spectacles. "Do you understand, my boy?"

"Ja!" said Jan. "Och, ja!" And he rushed over and hugged her.

He told me he couldn't explain it, but suddenly he didn't feel irritated any more, but very loving and protective, as if she was the child and he was centuries older and wiser. She had not understood what he understood; what poor Olaf had understood. She had not seen, she would never see, what they so clearly saw. What if Corinna did spend the rest of her life biting her way through hard little apples? She, at least, had had her long, golden day when all Elysium was hers in which to dilly-dally most deliciously just as she pleased.

How could Jan explain all this to our Oma, looking at him with kind, troubled eyes.

So he hugged her again, and left it at that.

Now since I left school I had been working in the office of a great tobacco firm. I hated it, but the pay was more than good, so I stuck it until I had saved thirty pounds, which was a very handsome sum in those days, at least it was to me. Then I handed in a month's notice; and one bleak December morning I sewed my savings in a little calico bag that I tacked inside my vest, next to my skin, so that I could feel it was safe; and off I went to Amsterdam to stay with Oma.

And I remember that the head clerk of my department, a brisk efficient woman, clearly showed that she thought my family *most* peculiar, allowing a young woman of my age to throw up a good job, and take a holiday abroad, in December, too, of all months!

But how wrong that sensible woman was! I shall never forget that winter holiday, never.

The day I arrived, an icy wind came whistling across the polders; the lowering skies cleared; and hour by hour, the canals and grachts froze harder and harder.

The next morning, the papers announced, on the front pages, that the ice was now hard enough to bear skaters. And up from every Dutch throat rose a great shout of joy! Schools straightway declared an "ice-holiday" and shut their doors. Offices closed early. So did the shops. Servants asked for time off, with a look on their faces that said they were going anyway. And down to the grachts, the canals, and the frozen rivers, we all tore, determined to make the most of the ice whilst it lasted.

Rika, Mina and Toje, our all-Dutch cousins, could, of course, skate most beautifully; but Jan and I had to learn. For a time we zig-zagged cautiously along, pushing old chairs in front of us; or persuaded obliging experts to tow us along on a rope. Then we tried on our own. We slithered and fell and all but broke our necks a thousand times; till suddenly, the miracle happened, first to me, and then to Jan. We could skate! Skate!

I shall never forget the wild triumph of that moment, the joy of belonging at last to that new wintry world where everyone skimmed and flew, and the trees, silver-stiff on the banks, cast blue and violet shadows before our flying feet. Everything else belonged to another world, commonplace and dull. All that really counted was our crisp, shining days on the ice. All our talk was of skating and skaters; of students setting out at dawn from Rotterdam to skate all the way to Gouda to buy long, clay pipes; and then triumphantly skating home again, clay pipes still unbroken in their hands; and champions in Friesland who flew like arrows along their frozen rivers outstripping any train that ran on rails.

Then there was the gratifying behaviour of the young man who served in the draper's shop at the corner of Oma's road. An awkward, lumbering young man on land, but now, on skates, he became a positive swallow; and was forever hovering round us four girls, scratching words of love on the ice as he twisted and span.

But which one of us he so adored, we never knew, for he always shot off when we approached. And small wonder either, for we heartlessly spelled his fond messages aloud, with shrieks of unfeeling laughter.

With all this on hand we naturally took scant notice at first of a first-class family to-do that seemed to be simmering away every time we raced home to snatch a hasty meal. But presently even we began to be aware that Oma was growing downright annoyed with our Tanta Joh.

Now I ought to explain that Tanta Joh had always been considered the beauty of the family. She was a tall, well-made woman with really beautiful eyes and an attractive, spontaneous smile. True, she had suffered bitterly during the war. She still sincerely mourned her handsome sailor-husband, but now she felt safe again in Oma's comfortable home, and also, thanks no doubt to Oma's comfortable meals, she had blossomed into a most attractive widow; and there were, it seemed, certain offers of marriage.

Now offers of marriage are not lightly made in Holland even to-day, and in those days they were even more formal. One of these, we gathered, had actually been made through a lawyer who had carefully set down all his client had to offer our Tanta Joh, including, I remember, a tea-plantation across the seas in Sumatra.

But Tanta Joh was behaving very strangely. On one hand, she frankly admitted she would like to get married again. Gottlieb himself would have wished it. And it wasn't good for Jan to have no man in his life.

"That's the idea!" grinned Jan. "Blame me for my own step-papa!"

But Oma sharply told him to hold his tongue, and went on to say that Tanta Joh simply had to make up her mind. Potvordikkie! One didn't keep expensive lawyers hanging about waiting for an answer!

But Tanta Joh refused to be hurried, even by the expensive lawyer; and day by day Oma grew crosser and crosser.

Now, of course, I realise that poor Oma knew in her heart that Tanta Joh would be far happier married. She was an affectionate, warm-hearted woman, born to have a man, a home of her own to cherish. Why then waste precious time with no fewer than three respectable gentlemen only too willing, too anxious to lay their middle-aged hearts and steady incomes at Tanta Joh's feet?

We girls, however, all in our unfeeling twenties, confided in each other that all three gentlemen must be touched by Little Lotty, which is the Dutch way of saying a little weak in the head. Wanting to marry our Tanta Joh indeed, nice-looking though she was! Why, the woman was all of forty-five!

Oddly enough, Jan said very little; even when we heard that Tanta Joh had definitely turned down the gentleman with the tea-plantation in Sumatra, and Mina said, "Ha! she's probably found out he's got a couple of tea-coloured wives over there as well!"

Then late one evening we were all drinking hot chocolate at a little stall set up on the ice, when Rika yelped, "Look! Just look!"

There, skating along in excellent style, came a whole family. The man led the way, and behind him, in a line, skated a woman and four boys in order of size. Each held his right hand correctly on his back, left hand clasping the hand on the back before him.

But it was the woman, the woman, who sang out the orders that kept them swinging along in such gay, fine rhythm.

Then we recognised them. It was Mynheer Vos, quiet retiring Mynheer Vos, who had lost his wife that night in the terrible fog. Yes, it was Mynheer Vos and his four motherless boys.

And the woman was Tanta Joh!

Tanta Joh . . .!

We looked at Jan. He was smiling, a queer crooked smile.

Then he stooped to re-tie his skates. As he straightened up again, he caught my eye.

"Now!" he said. "Now, what will our Oma say if Corinna takes on that little orchard?"

Then he was off, shouting to us to follow him.

Chapter IX

TOUR DE FRANCE

That Easter, our handsome Tanta Joh married the widower, Mynheer Kees Willem Vos.

At first Oma couldn't get over it. Oh, she had nothing against the man. He was all right . . . in his quiet way. But there were those four imps of boys and all the work they meant. When Tanta Joh could have married so comfortably, too! Been waited on hand and foot! Not to mention the "substantial provision for any eventualities" thoughtfully listed in the inducements of the expensive lawyer.

Whereas now, well, Tanta Joh would have her apron on from morning till night. Potvordikkie! sighed Oma, her mouth was full of teeth. She then rounded on me, demanding to know why I was smiling. I truthfully said I didn't know I was. I didn't add that I was thinking that when a Dutch woman says her mouth is full of teeth, she is flabbergasted all right, but not precisely speechless.

But if Oma's mouth was full of teeth, her heart was fortunately in its usual place. And before long, though she would have died rather than admit it, she was positively revelling in her four ready-made new grandsons. There they were, right on her doorstep, and very respectful indeed to their new Oma who so briskly ordered them to wipe their feet, use their handkerchiefs, stop scuffing on her clean

floor, and sit down do, and eat up the tarts or cakes she'd
spent half an evening baking for them—when she wasn't
patching their shirts or refeeting their socks.

As for Tanta Joh, there could be no doubt at all about
her happiness. Aprons suited her. I had never seen her look
so cheerful, so competent. Indeed, when I think of my
Tanta Joh, I feel angry that the world over the very name of
step-mother has come to mean something almost sinister.
Yet there must be many a woman who has brought nothing
but love and comfort into a forlorn and motherless home,
as she did. As she most certainly did.

Then it tickled everybody to see how, from the start,
Jan was nothing short of a hero to all four little boys. It
was: "Jan says so. Jan says I can. Jan says that's the way
to fix it."

And I remember once seeing one of them getting the
worst of a scrap, and yelling, "Wait! You just wait!
My big brother's going to teach me to box—with my
feet!"

But there was something about Jan himself that puzzled
me. He was always friendly and polite to his step-father,
but I noticed he still called him Mynheer and I sometimes
caught a look in his eye that baffled me.

Then one evening we were having a cup of coffee outside a café, and I happened to mention that it was Mynheer
Vos's birthday on Sunday, and Oma was wondering what
to buy him.

"Slippers," said Jan.

It was the way he said it, the harsh brittle note in his
voice, that made me put down my cup.

"I don't understand you," I said. "I just don't understand
you."

"That's not surprising," said Jan. "I don't understand myself, either."

It was almost dark. I couldn't see his face. And for a moment we were silent.

"Odd, isn't it?" said Jan presently. "Sometimes I loathe my mother marrying that nice little man. I look at him, and I want to kick his teeth in. Then other times, I want to hug him, to give him a gold watch and chain, I feel so grateful!

"Ja, ja! Grateful! But, of course, you wouldn't understand. You are not an only child. How can you understand the terrible responsibility of an only child whose father is dead?

"Mein Gott! Mein Gott! How I hate being responsible! And how I have hated myself for hating to be responsible. Work that out, if you can. Worst of all, how I have loathed being tied eternally to a nice safe job, because I know I shall feel like a criminal if I hand in my notice again.

"But now things are different. Yes, indeed. No more lying awake at night wishing I wasn't so important to my mother. For one thing, she deserves more than me, far more. So thank you, Lord, for my four dear little step-brothers and my good step-papa. For now I can take a job abroad.

"Abroad! Java! China, America, all over the world I'll go, until I find the place to live."

He broke off abruptly, and gave a little laugh.

"Such interesting postcards I'll send home," he said, but now his voice was altogether different, as if he was dismissing all he had said as rather amusing.

"And photographs, too, of course. Me, drinking licorice in Syria! Me, riding a camel in Arabia! Me, eating birds' nests in China!"

He laughed again. Then a waiter came out and switched

on the lights. And a friend passing by gave us a shout, and came over to join us.

And never again for many a long year did I come so close to my Cousin Jan.

I went back to England that Whitsuntide to find another job. I had come to the end of my thirty pounds, and I wasn't going to live on Oma.

She came to the station to see me off, of course.

Dear Oma! I can see her now, her kind, wrinkled face, her big, sensible handkerchief as she pretended to be only blowing her nose; and I can hear her voice, "Totziens! Totziens!"

But there was to be no re-seeing. Six months later, our Oma died in her sleep.

And this is strange—the evening before, she must have been going through her old photographs for there was a little pile of them on the table by her bed; all her four children when babies in stiff embroidered dresses and wide tartan sashes. But propped up against her lamp was an old faded yellow photograph that none of us had ever seen, the last one Oma must have seen before she fell asleep—our Oma herself and her poor Olaf . . . young, smiling, and tenderly holding hands.

A month later we had a postcard from Jan, a picture postcard of a great ugly factory. And on the back he had written:

Best greetings from Ploesti in Rumania. Interesting job in oil refinery here. JAN.

"M'm!" said my father. "Could be most interesting, if he has the sense to stay there, of course."

I didn't say a word, but as I studied that great, ugly factory, that queer foreign stamp, it was Jan I saw, Jan, suitcase in hand, eagerly setting out on his quest for the place to live.

And now, as the months went by, and there were no more long letters from Oma to link us all together, I am afraid the whole family gradually drifted into sending odd postcards to each other, and a photograph or two from time to time.

I remember we had a really beautiful photograph of our French cousins, Paul and Philippe, on their wedding-day. They married sisters, Simone and Colette.

The Dutch girls were the next to get married, all three to solid, sensible-looking Dutchmen. And from them, too, we always had cards for Christmas and for our birthdays; and, by and by, snapshots of their babies.

As for us three in England: William, now in the Civil Service, married an English girl; my sister took up nursing; and I tried out a variety of jobs. And I was now sampling one in a "Ye Olde Shoppe" which claimed to stock everything for "Ye Artes and Craftes".

One summer day, quite by accident, I picked up a newspaper that somebody had left on a seat in the park where I sometimes ate my mid-day sandwiches. To my delight, it was a French paper. But it wasn't the gripping story of the lady accused of tipping her unfaithful lover down a well that made me forget my sandwiches baking away in the sun, it was a sober advertisement tucked away in one corner of the back page that I read again and again, and then carefully tore out and put in my purse.

And with my head still full of that advertisement, and twenty-five minutes late, I went back to "Ye Olde Shoppe"; politely agreed with my irate employer that I wasn't cut out for "Artes and Craftes", handed over my artistic green smock, and went home to compose a careful letter, and copy out the three best of my testimonials.

A month later, thanks to that stray French newspaper, I was teaching English and a very ladylike sort of Swedish Drill, in a girls' school in Alençon in Normandy.

I dropped a card, of course, to Paul and Philippe; and back came two very friendly letters saying, "You will spend all your holidays with us, of course!"

But my salary was precisely thirty shillings a month, plus my keep and laundry, so it didn't look as if I would be able to afford a trip down to Marseilles for many a long month.

Then the school in Alençon was run by an efficient, formidable woman called Madame Meunier, who promptly informed me that I would do well to realise from the start that she stood for no stuff and nonsense about "girls will be girls". Under her roof, girls were fee-paying pupils with examinations to pass, and parents who very properly demanded results for the good money they laid out—combined with the strictest supervision of health, and suitable recreation, of course. That's where the Swedish Drill came in, I gathered.

So, from eight sharp every morning till seven in the evening, we were all kept hard at it. But I was happy enough, thanks to a lively young woman about my own age, called Monique Bobet. She taught Music throughout the school: Piano, Violin, Voice-training, and Tonic Solfa.

Her parents ran the school in a village some five miles or so from Alençon. Papa had charge of all the boys; Maman educated the girls. They were friendly, kindly people, who always made me very welcome when Monique took me home with her to spend our afternoons off.

Now one warm sunny day that July, I was in my tiny bedroom, window wide open, washing my hair, when in raced Monique. To my surprise she was wearing her Sunday best—hat and gloves as well as costume; and she was carrying a bulky canvas valise.

"Ah no!" she screamed. "Not washing you hair *again*! Dry it at once! Hurry! Hurry!"

She slung down the valise, shot over to the window, and shut it tight.

"Listen, I've seen the old camel, and I've arranged everything with her, simply everything!"

And before I had time to inquire just what she had arranged with Madame our Head Mistress, Monique was rattling on:

"Don't stand there gaping like a fish! Dry that hair, and I'll get out your things. We're going now! Now, I tell you, this very minute! She has given us the whole beautiful afternoon off, as well as to-morrow! Somebody must have left her some money. And I have a wonderful idea, a positive inspiration!"

As she spoke, she flung open my wardrobe door, brought out my Sunday costume and hat—in those days we always had one dedicated rig-out. And then she wheeled round, tore the counterpane off my bed, ripped off a blanket, and began to stuff it into the valise.

"I've taken one off my bed, too," she began. And then caught sight of my face.

"Triple idiot!" she squealed. "I'm not pinching them! Maman has piles of them at home, enough for an orphanage."

"Then why take these?"

"Because we're not going home," panted Monique, struggling with the bulging valise. "Ah no, not this time!

You and I are going to see the Tour de France. Yes, dear
Miss, the Tour de France!"

"What!" I said. "The bicycle-race?"

Monique flung up both arms.

"Mon Dieu! Listen to her! She says 'the bicycle-race',
as if it were an affair of nothing at all. Let me tell you, you
ignorant Miss, all France, except this hole of a school, all
Europe is now palpitating, suffocating with excitement
about this bicycle-race. They let the best prisoners out of
jail; they carry out the sick on stretchers; they stand four
deep along the roads of France; simply everybody really
living will be out to see it pass."

I said yes, I'd noticed the newspapers were full of it.
But how were we two going to see it? The race wasn't going
through Alençon.

"No," said Monique. "But to-morrow morning at ten-
thirty-three, it is due to arrive at Caen."

"Caen!" I said; and I opened my purse and tipped out all
I had, about seven and sixpence. And I said I didn't think
that was going to cover my fare and a bed for the night,
even if we did provide our own blankets.

Beds! hooted Monique. We weren't going to waste
money on beds. And for the love of Heaven, would I get
into my clothes and stop asking questions. She had everything arranged, everything, including a loaf of bread, some
hard-boiled eggs, a beautiful piece of sausage, and a bottle
of cider, right there, under the blankets in the valise. And
yes, I simply had to wear my Sunday best or the old camel
might smell a rat, and she'd burst all her seams if she guessed
what was in Monique's head, not to mention the valise.

And oh, all right, if I *must* know, we were taking the
train to a village some seven miles out of Caen, if one could

call it a village, three shops, a café and a church, but all of it right there on the route of the RACE. And nearby was a beautiful, convenient forest, where we two were going to sleep that night.

And think of it, carolled Monique, moon shining, nightingales warbling, and we two picnicking away, and straightway falling into a delicious slumber. Then, at crack of dawn, up we'd spring, fresh as daisies, with absolutely first choice of a place from which to view the RACE.

And now would I hurry, or must she fall on her knees to implore me to give over behaving like the Rock of Gibraltar?

So I pushed my wet hair under my hat, anchored it down with two long hat-pins, pulled on my gloves, and off we went.

But the joyous smiles froze on our faces when we reached the bottom of the stairs; there, crossing the hall, was Madame our Head Mistress.

"Ah, so there you are! Well, Mademoiselle, be sure to give my kindest regards to Monsieur and Madame, your parents."

Monique said she would indeed, and such was the respectful gratitude in her voice that Madame positively thawed.

"Listen," she said, "I think, yes, I feel sure that we can also manage Sunday evening without you. No, you need not return until Monday morning. That will give you a really long week-end. But kindly see you are here by eight o'clock on Monday, of course."

We assured her we would; and still smiling most gratefully, we sedately walked out with the valise wedged between us, before Madame our Head Mistress had time to consider its remarkable bulk and shape.

But once on the road to the station, Monique fairly danced with excitement.

"Can't you see what this means? Now, when we've seen the race pass through our village, we can take the bus down to Caen, spend the whole day there, and catch the last train back home. I'll send Papa and Maman a postcard from the station, explaining everything. Yes, of course, they'll get it. A cousin of Maman's keeps the post-office. He'll read it and take it round to them. He always does."

So we sent the postcard to her Maman and Papa, warning them we'd be arriving late on Sunday to spend the night with them; and then we boarded a train to that village some seven miles from Caen. And we had our picnic under the stars in the nearby wood; and then tried hard to drop into that delicious slumber.

Nowadays young people all over France often camp out like this so as to have first choice of a place from which to view this great cycle-race. But in our day, it simply was *not* done, least of all by respectable, young school-mistresses. And I lay there, curled up in my blanket on my bed of dry bracken, looking up at my Sunday costume dangling on a branch over my head, wondering what Madame our Head Mistress would say if she could see us now. And I felt so chilly, I got up and put on my jacket.

When dawn crawled round at last, we pulled on our skirts, combed our hair, packed our valise, and set off for the village.

And suddenly, why, we weren't stiff and cross any more. The sun was shining; the birds were singing at the tops of their voices; the air was crisp and sweet; and in ten minutes' time we'd be sitting outside that café, ordering bowls of coffee and hunks of bread and a great dish of butter.

Fortified and cheered, we would then stake our claim to the best possible place on all that long road from which to behold the Tour de France. Oh, life was wonderful! And we lifted up our voices with the startled birds, and sang our glad Te Deum, too, with words and music that ranged from "Au ciel! Au ciel!" to "Ma Normandie".

Nobody was in the least surprised to see us sit down so early outside the Café du Bois Vert. Indeed, the café was already buzzing with customers, all talking about the Race, of course.

We, therefore, lost no time in devouring our breakfast, and by half-past seven, there we were, in an excellent place; most cunningly selected, from which we would see the Race come round a great bend in the road, and sweep down a steep hill into the valley below.

By eight o'clock we were warmly congratulating ourselves on our excellent foresight; for now both sides of the road were lined three deep with spectators. And every man among them seemed to have trustworthy, inside information about the tricks those cyclists from Belgium, Holland, Luxembourg, North Africa, Italy and Switzerland had up their sleeves; more interesting still, they all knew precisely how the French Giants of the Road were proposing to outsmart them.

From this we proceeded to exchange even more piquant "one says" about every cyclist's form, age, Christian names, love-affairs, and other interesting details.

Presently, however, we all felt in the need of something more substantial. So we sat down to polish off sausage, bread, hard-boiled eggs, and bottles of cider and wine—luckily Monique and I still had the remains of our picnic left at the bottom of our valise. And as we ate and passed round the bottles, we debated the merits of cold tea, tonic water and lemonade for quenching the thirst. Not ours, of course— but the far more serious thirst of professional cyclists.

We then spoke our minds about the official lunches provided for these Giants of the Road. Why not suppress such fripperies as fruit-tarts, for instance, and treat them all to a nourishing bottle of egg-yolks beaten up in champagne? Why not, indeed!

A middle-aged gentleman immediately behind us then held our side of the road spellbound with stories of the early days of the Tour when racing went on far into the night; and under cover of darkness certain ignoble competitors thought nothing of hopping into a train with their bicycles, staggering everybody by arriving, oh, so fresh and early, miles and miles in front of the honest ones still sweating away far behind . . . till somebody tumbled to their little game.

Then there was that memorable year when feelings rose so high that gentlemen in motor-cars had to clear the route, brandishing and firing off pistols as they went.

And that other momentous year when a kind-hearted competitor called Julien Moineau instructed his friends to set cans of beer all along one parched section of the route where one choked down thick dust with every breath one drew. So naturally every poor devil on wheels slowed up here and there to snatch a can or two of free beer. All except our kind Julien Moineau! He couldn't be seen for dust as he streaked ahead, well in the lead, to cheering Bordeaux, and the yellow sweater.

I asked why a yellow sweater; and Monique hurriedly apologised for me, saying I was English and she hadn't had the time yet to explain that the winner of each lap of the

race always had the honour of wearing a beautiful yellow
sweater. But, naturally, if he lost the next lap, he had to
take it off and hand it over to the winner.

Loud cheers drowned the rest of her explanations. The
police had arrived to clear all stragglers from the road.

Half an hour later, stiff with excitement, we really let
rip. Round the bend came a great procession, a cavalcade of
gaily decorated publicity vans and cars. Klaxons sounding,
megaphones blaring, accordions playing, they swept before
us.

Ladies and gentlemen! Soothe that liver! Drink So-and-
So's ultra-limpid Tonic Water! The water that will make
YOU sparkle and sing!

Ladies, make that love-letter permanent! Use So-and-So's
ink!

Try the cheese made from the milk of our smiling cows!
Win her heart! Use So-and-So's brilliantine!

Suddenly I gave a scream. Nobody heard me, of course.
So I shook Monique by the arm.

"That blue van," I yelled. "That man on the top!"

"The one blowing a bugle?" screamed back Monique.

"Yes! Yes! I do believe, yes, I'm sure . . . that's my
Cousin Jan!"

Chapter X

A CANDLE FOR SAINT ANTHONY

Yes, there on the roof of a sky-blue van, joyously blowing a bugle, sat my Cousin Jan—or his double. But before I had time to make absolutely certain, the van was out of sight, swallowed up in the noisy caravan, now sweeping down into the valley below.

"But you said that cousin of yours was in Rumania refining oil or something!" screamed Monique. "It's this sun. You're seeing things."

And it was no use screaming back that even with a sun-stroke I'd recognise a cousin when I saw one, for she wasn't listening. She, and everyone else, were now holding their breath, tense with excitement. The last car, the last van, had gone hooting past, and the road lay empty, silent, waiting.

"A-ah!" breathed the crowd.

And round the bend came the first cyclists, wheels spinning, heads bent, bright jerseys flaming, gloved hands on curving handlebars.

On either side, on motor-bikes or in cars, rode the gentlemen of the press, note-books at the ready, cameras in hand, very haggard and spent.

But nobody else noticed *them*. All eyes were riveted on that dazzling rainbow of cyclists now spinning along the white, dusty road.

"Vive! Vive!" they shouted. "Courage! You'll wear that yellow jersey yet! Pedal, boys, pedal!"

"What a speed!" exulted the gentleman behind us. "What a yawning tomb of a speed!"

And at that yawning tomb of a speed, the cyclists sped past, sometimes alone, sometimes in groups. And there was beauty, drama, a fierce poetry in those spinning wheels, those gay thin bodies curved in flight. And I heard myself shouting too, "Courage! Courage! Pedal, boys, pedal!"

Suddenly, almost abruptly, it was all over. But no, round the bend, came one last cyclist, a French one, right leg bandaged, face grey and grim, but streaking along so gamely that every heart rushed straight out to him.

"Vas-y!" we roared. "It's for France! Courage! You won't be the tail-light long!"

"Pity!" said the gentleman behind us. "A thousand pities we haven't a nice bucket of cold water to tip over him. It would have been just the thing."

But now, round our bend, rolled a magnificent Red Cross ambulance, so we cheered that, too.

"Ah!" said the gentleman, a shade regretfully, I thought. "That wasn't needed here this time. But last year, now, one of the Italians skidded as he swung round this very bend, and p-ss! shot like a swallow right over his handlebars. And landed in that little quarry down there. Naturally, we were all crossing ourselves, getting ready for the Prayers for the Dead, when up rose our Italian, and then knelt down for a moment to say a pious thank you to his good Italian angel. I tell you, the tears were streaming down our faces. Ah yes, one can miss many such a dramatic moment if one just sits outside a café, waiting, down there in Caen.

"On the other hand, of course, up here one renounces all

the emotions of the Arrival. Flowers, kisses, speeches, music, cheers . . . absolutely palpitating! No, one really doesn't know what to decide."

"Come on!" whispered Monique, and tugged my arm. So we said goodbye to the knowledgeable gentleman, and joined in the crowd now fighting to get on the bus to Caen. By some miracle, we managed to squeeze inside. Four on a seat we sat, or stood on each other's feet, packed like matches in a box. And off we bounced through a sprawling tangle of cars and cycles, all making our way down to Caen.

"Listen!" shouted Monique—she had to, the din in our bus was terrific. "We'll look for him, if you like. Everything is stopping the night in Caen. Resting!"

Resting! You could have heard Caen resting a mile away.

Every square, every street, every available space was crammed with vans and cars. Gramophones blared. On improvised stages, music-hall stars sang and played accordions; and salesmen shouted, and showered samples to right and to left.

Ladies! Our knitting-wool is pure and soft as an angel's wing.

This insecticide kills all that creeps and crawls.

See your face in your furniture! Try a tin!

"But tell me," I asked, as we struggled through the crowds, "where are all the cyclists?"

"Resting, of course," said Monique. "Ah, come on!"

She grabbed my arm, and led me across the road. There, outside a small hotel-restaurant, was a dense throng, chanting: Hector! Léon! Hector! Léon!

Presently the door opened, and out came two cyclists. And one of them was wearing the yellow sweater! A little girl ran forward, holding out a great bunch of roses. And the victor, taking it, stooped to kiss her on both cheeks. And we, of course, went delirious with joy and emotion.

"Listen!" said Monique, eyes shining like stars. "How much money have you got left?"

"Two shillings," I said. "And my return ticket."

"Good!" said Monique. "We'll eat here, even if it is only an omelette. Then we can say all the rest of our lives that we have eaten under the same roof as THEM."

But we simply couldn't get inside that restaurant; in fact we had to be content with the last two seats on the pavement outside.

And we were just about to start on our modest omelette, when I saw him again! My Cousin Jan . . . or his double.

He was drinking his coffee at a table in a corner of the crowded terrace. I looked and looked. That square head . . . those dancing blue eyes . . .

But now, I wasn't so sure. After all, I hadn't seen Jan for years. This young man was so like him, and yet so unlike. So well-dressed, so casual, so sure of himself.

Then he noticed us looking at him. And smiled.

"That proves it!" hissed Monique. "That is *not* the smile one gives to one's cousin! He thinks . . . Oh, for the love of Heaven, let's get on with our food!"

But I had thought of something else. And I began to search in my handbag for something I had carried round with me ever since I was a child, just as one carries a crooked sixpence or some other odd charm.

"Ah, non!" gasped Monique, very alarmed.

It was the whistle, one of the little whistles Jan had brought us from Germany, one each for Oma's nine grand-children, that year we were all on holiday in Amsterdam.

I held it out on the palm of my hand, as if showing it to

Monique, as if pointing out the figure nine scratched deep upon it. And out of the corner of my eye, I watched the young man.

The mocking smile vanished. He was now staring hard at me, and then at the whistle. Then he got up, and threaded his way through the table towards us.

"Pardonnez-moi, mesdemoiselles," he began, "mais est-ce-possible . . ."

"Ja!" I cried. "Of course it is possible!"

And turning to Monique, I proudly said, "Permit me to introduce my Cousin Jan!"

Yes, this tall fine young man was my Cousin Jan. And at first we could do nothing but shake hands and exclaim, "Now! Now, can this be true?" Till Monique said perhaps Monsieur-my-cousin-fallen-from-the-skies would care to sit down at our table and finish his coffee.

So Jan called for coffee for all three of us. And I explained why I was in France; and gave him all the latest news from England.

And he explained that Rumania was not the place to live, at least not for him, and how he now had an interesting job with a French firm that dealt in lubricating-oil. Yes, that was their van we had seen. He and two colleagues took it in turn to drive, blow the bugle, and hand out the sales-talk and samples.

Then he showed me the latest photograph of Tanta Joh with her husband and the four boys, all big lads now, and all smartly dressed in what Monique called "le costume-golfe".

"Intelligent youngsters!" laughed Jan. "They still think the world of me!

"But seriously," he went on. "I would never have recognised you—but for the whistle."

Monique said maybe it was the way I did my hair now. She'd had to bully me into it, of course! But so much smarter, didn't Monsieur Jan think so?

Monsieur Jan said he did, indeed; and what about a stroll round now?

So we got up; and Jan paid our bill, too, from a most impressive wallet bulging with notes. And off we strolled, one each side of him, joyously accepting paper-hats, dabs of perfume, samples of tooth-paste, boxes of liver-pills, sporting newspapers, and everything else that was offered us.

Presently we came to the sky-blue van parked under the plane-trees of one of the crowded squares. And Jan's two colleagues caught sight of him, one cousinly arm round me, the other round Monique; and they immediately broke off yelling the praises of their lubricating-oil, and swept off their straw hats, and jumped down to shake hands with us.

And when Jan introduced me as his first cousin from England, they said, "Enchanted!" and one of them murmured, "Remind me to mention it to my first aunt from America!" And we all burst out laughing; and they said, to blazes with publicity, their own throats needed lubricating. And they slung the bugle inside the van, and we all crossed the square and sat down outside a café there to drink something cool.

And Monique's dark eyes grew wider and wider as they regaled us with fantastic stories of the Tour, and other lesser races; how they knew one Dutch cyclist who daily defended himself against the "Hunger Knock" by consuming seven mutton-chops, one dozen ham sandwiches, one dozen bananas, not to mention the fried legs of six chickens as in America, one quart of porridge as in Scotland, one quart of rice-pudding as in England, all washed down by two quarts of coffee as in Holland—and all outside his regular meals as in France, of course!

Then Jan described the cyclists resting away, the honoured guests of the best hotels, surrounded by team-managers, time-keepers, doctors, masseurs, barbers, reporters and photographers, as they relaxed, chin-deep, in Somebody's Soapsuds, drinking Somebody's Tonic Water or taking bites of Somebody's Chocolate, before they were escorted to the ping-pong table, on which they climbed to be massaged with Somebody's Muscle Reviver.

And all the while, their devoted mechanics would be slaving away, stripping their cycles, oiling and screwing everything together again, before they examined every centimetre of the tyres; and declared each cycle to be in first-class racing order.

Then, said Jan, the hotel manager with all his staff, and of course all the photographers, would escort the Giants of the Road to the best bedrooms where they would sink back on Somebody's Spring Mattresses, cycles leaning against their pillows, to have their photographs taken all over again.

At this point, Jan caught sight of my face.

"Look at my cousin!" he roared. "Do you observe the look on her face? She is saying to herself, 'Och, our Jan is still the same wonderful liar!' When I assure you, all I do is tell the truth as I see it!"

Then he called to the waiter. "Now, you'll bear me out, won't you? They *do* take their bikes to bed with them, don't they?"

The waiter cautiously said well, some did, and some left this sacred charge to their trusted mechanics, who undoubtedly slept with them—with one eye well open, of course.

Then he held out a monumental menu, and hinted that maybe we were now ready for dinner.

Jan and his two friends closely studied this document, and after much earnest consultation with the waiter, it was decided that for our main course we would all have something called "Bifteck Tour de France".

It turned out to be a beef-steak decorated with a bicycle—wheels made of slices of tomato; handlebars, frame, and rider piped in mayonnaise.

And there we sat, and talked and laughed, and ate our good dinner, merrily taking our time. And up and down surged the crowds; and louder and merrier grew the sales-talk, the gramophones, and the municipal brass-band, now playing away for dear life in front of the Town Hall.

Presently Monique looked at her watch and gasped, Mon Dieu! We'd have to fly like the wind or we'd lose our last train. And her Papa would throw a fit if we didn't turn up as she had faithfully promised on her postcard. Very old-fashioned, her poor Papa!

I hadn't the time to wonder if her old-fashioned Papa would ever know of our night out under the stars, for we were now tearing over to the sky-blue van. In we climbed, and sat up on the driver's seat with Marcel. Jan and Max climbed up on the roof. And off we drove to the station, horn and bugle going full blast, as the crowds scattered before us.

We snatched the valise from the cloakroom in record time, scrambled into the waiting train, and off it steamed.

And we leaned out of the window, calling "Au-revoir! Et merci! Merci!"

And they ran alongside the train waving their straw-hats, and Jan began to sing a German ballad that goes:

> *Forsaken! Forsaken! Forsaken am I!*
> *Like the stone in the church-yard,*
> *Forsaken am I.*

And they all three took it up and sang:

> *Forsaken! Forsaken! Forsaken are we!*
> *Like three stones in the church-yard,*
> *Forsaken we three!*

The train gathered speed, and shot ahead. And when we could see their straw-hats no longer, we sank down on the hard wooden seats; and Monique sighed that everything had been wonderful, absolutely wonderful! We had seen the Tour de France; we had met my Cousin Jan; we'd eaten a heavenly dinner; and now she was madly, gloriously in love. But she couldn't, however, decide at the moment whom she adored most, Hector, Léon, Jan, Marcel or Max. They were all so perfectly marvellous.

And she took out her purse and began to count her money.

"Good!" she said. "Just enough for a candle, a beautiful candle for my darling Saint Anthony. I asked him to see we had a nice day. And I've told you dozens of times how obliging he is at finding things, but even I didn't expect him to find your Cousin Jan for us as well."

Chapter XI

THE IRONMONGERY OF THE
RUE SAINT LOUIS

At eight sharp that Monday morning, Madame our Head Mistress looked at the watch pinned on her majestic bosom, nodded, and said, "Ah, so there you are! And I see the rest has done you good. Nothing like a quiet week-end in the country to repose the nerves."

We respectfully agreed, and demurely went on up the stairs to take off our Sunday best, dress for duty, and replace the blankets on our beds.

And Monique, mournfully buttoning herself into her grey linen overall, complained that one breath of this desiccated school-air, and hop! our blissful week-end vanished like dew on the grass. But, thank the good God, the holidays were now in sight. Another fifteen and a half days, and life would cease to be an eternal toiling up the First Steps to Music with a pack of heavy-weights who needed muzzling not voice-training.

And wouldn't it be a dream, sighed Monique, if during this holiday we both met handsome young men with wonderful jobs and discerning mothers who implored them to marry us quick before somebody else snatched us up.

And oh, imagine the exquisite bliss of composing a telegram to the old camel:

Adieu for ever! Off on my honeymoon!

A loud and insistent bell dourly shattered this entrancing day-dream; and we went down to breakfast and duty.

And Madame our Head Mistress, handing me my coffee, said reproachfully, "But you sound quite hoarse, Miss! I trust you have not caught cold?"

I hastily said no, I didn't think so; and realised I was indeed croaking. But I didn't need the swift warning kick Monique so promptly gave me. I had no honest intentions whatever of explaining it was all due to twelve uproarious hours of cheering, laughing, and talking. Nor did I mention meeting my Cousin Jan. Something told me Madame our Head Mistress would disapprove of all masculine cousins—no matter how genuine and unforeseen.

Oddly enough, neither of us ever returned to that school in Alençon. During those holidays, Monique *did* meet an eager young man, a school-master who, it seemed, had been positively praying to meet a girl just like Monique to take back with him to Morocco, where he had an excellent job waiting for him—if suitably married to another qualified teacher who would take over the younger pupils.

"And we are truly in love," wrote Monique. "I swear we are. So everything is absolutely perfect. Why not come and stay with us? I'm sure we could arrange something just as wonderful for you."

But I gratefully wrote back that I, too, had met a young man. And though he freely admitted, being English, that he hadn't been exactly praying to meet a girl just like me, he was paying me the compliment of behaving as if he had. And by Christmas we, too, were married.

Now Jan, by this time, had waved farewell to the lubricating business, and was working in Italy as a Sworn

Translator, at least that is how he styled himself. And Tanta Joh wrote to my mother that this meant that he was sworn to eternal secrecy about the vital documents entrusted to him for translation. And that she did hope he wasn't over-working, as he was also giving lessons in German, French, and English.

The Sworn Translator found time, however, to send me a wedding-present. I still have it—a handsome black satin table-runner with hand-painted yellow stars glittering all over it. And with it came a poem—a poem in English.

To My Cousin on Her Marriage

Do you recall how children nine
Once sang to their Oma in verses fine?
Sang how their Grandpa at any time
Could take up his pen and write wishes in rhyme?
Alas, to rhyme in English is, I fear,
Devilishly hard for me, my dear.
Yet I cannot resist the strong temptation
To borrow his pen on this great occasion.
So, as poor Olaf would say,
In his poetical way,
The blessing of the Lord be on this pair.
May love and happiness be ever their share.
And now to give a token of my own devotion,
I thought and thought, till came this notion:
That not alone by day we love the light,
We love the stars that shine by night.
So I had this table-decker made,
With shining stars, each of a golden shade.
Take it! In affection I send it thee,
And seeing it, think kind of me!

JAN.

I still can't think why, but it was the hand-writing that touched me most—the careful, elaborate hand-writing, so different from Jan's customary, slap-dash scrawl.

And I was very nettled indeed to see my young husband, standing there, gaping at my beautiful table-runner and touching poem, and muttering "Good lord!" And then hastily adding, "Sounds a good sort, though."

Looking back now, it seems to me that from my wedding-day onwards, the years seemed to gather up speed and simply whisk along. We had two children, precious little money, and much quiet happiness.

And over there in Holland, Toje, Rika and Mina were quietly bringing up their little families, too; and so were Paul and Philippe in France.

None of us had the money to travel, but we went on exchanging cards at Christmas or the New Year, and now and again a letter and a photograph or two.

And my two children, looking at these photographs, would exclaim, "Help! I give up! You want a family-tree and an atlas to know who's who in Mummy's foreign relations."

And I suppose *their* puzzled children were saying the same sort of thing, too.

And I would find myself wondering what Oma would have thought of all these scattered great-grandchildren of hers, and I'd look at her faded photograph on the mantel-piece and promise myself—and her, that I simply would find the time to write more regularly to everyone in future.

But the years slipped away and in less than no time, or so it seemed to me, there was Philippe writing me one Christmas:

"Can you realise it? We grow middle-aged! All except

this vagabond, Jan! He still has no rope about his feet, he still travels on."

It was true; we were tranquilly growing middle-aged, all, except Jan. He still had no family ties to keep him in place; he still travelled on. And from time to time he would shower the whole family with gaudy picture postcards from the most unlikely places with unpronounceable names. I remember one in particular. It showed a group of fishermen wading in the sea, waving landing-nets with very long handles; and on the back was one of Jan's comprehensive news-flashes:

This shows fishing for amber in Baltic Sea. Here on business. Firm dealing in cigarette-holders. Very interesting. Love to all. Extra stamp for children. Jan.

Yes, Jan had become a rich and much appreciated source of foreign-stamps, a fine foreign Sindbad-the-Sailor of an uncle who rollicked round the world, obliging all the young stamp-collectors in the family as he went.

But over there in Holland, Tanta Joh would sigh over these cards, and write yet again to my mother, "I do wish our Jan would settle down, too! Why can't he see it is high time he now found a sensible wife, and started a family— like the others. So much more sensible!"

Then we heard that Mynheer Vos, Tanta Joh's husband, was retiring from business. An old aunt had left him a modest legacy, and with this, and their savings, they were buying a trim little house a few miles outside Rotterdam.

"Just a comfortable bus-ride," wrote Tanta Joh. "On a clear morning we can see the church-spires from our bed-room window. Not that we need go to Rotterdam. We have all the shops we want here. And so very quiet and peaceful. Just the place for retired people with not much income."

The very word "retirement" must have shocked Jan into realising that even *his* mother could grow old; and from then on, every year, he faithfully turned up in Holland to be with his mother on her birthday. As I have mentioned before, the Dutch set great store on birthdays, and now, the tenth of May, bringing Jan with it, became more and more of a shining red-letter day in our Tanta Joh's quiet life.

Now maybe you have noticed that so far I have only told you what I myself remember about my Cousin Jan. But now my tale must needs be different.

The black nightmare of the Second World War drew nearer and nearer; and then engulfed us all. And it was only a few months ago, when I was at last able to go back to France, that I learned something of what happened to my Cousin Jan.

Indeed, it was only then that I realised that all these early memories of mine were but fragments stored in my mind, as a child might treasure the bright pieces of some jig-saw puzzle. Here now were other pieces of Jan's story, some gay and amusing, some dark and terrible.

And if the brighter pieces seem to seek to redeem the dark misery of the others, this is none of my contriving. My Cousin Jan is one of that vast army of men who have no stomach whatever for reliving the grey desolation of any war, who have a way of dismissing the whole infernal business in a sentence or two.

On the other hand, however, they will dwell almost affectionately on some odd happening, some queer antic of war that raised a laugh in the very face of Death itself.

So I can only tell the rest as I heard it myself, or maybe I ought to say: as I saw it myself. For one summer night, my heart suddenly very warm within me, I recognised the fundamental piece, the shining key-piece of the story I was trying to fix together.

And overhead in the starry sky, Jan's Good Angel, seeing me so moved, doubtlessly bridled a little, and muttered that he, at least, had always had the sense to recognise that transcendent spark in my cousin that many waters could not quench—unaccountable customer though he had been at times.

The first new pieces of my story are set in the careless, unheeding years mid-way between the two World Wars. And they are bright and merry enough, for on them you must picture my Cousin Jan, spanking along the lovely roads of France again, but this time in a smart little sports-car that simply devoured the kilometres, and which had been lent to him, free of charge—together with an impressive leather brief-case full of coloured leaflets, by a German firm which specialised in stoves.

Yes, Jan was now a commercial traveller "in stoves", all colours, all sizes, and all with a solid reputation for reliability and the smallest of appetites, amiably digesting everything from potato-peelings to "briquettes" made of coal dust and cement. All of which, as French ironmongers were quick to recognise, made one overlook their regrettable Teutonic origin.

On his thirty-seventh birthday, Jan decided to spend the day in a quiet little town, not yet on his regular round, where there was one important ironmonger and two small but excellent restaurants. Jan not only felt the day had come to introduce his stoves to this unknown, important iron-monger, he felt even more strongly that the day called for something very special in lunches to console himself for being thirty-seven—an uninteresting age, far too near forty, and which had treacherously caught up on him, and he all unawares—or so he told himself that bright summer morning.

And now as he parked his car on the square before the church, he considered again the rival merits of the Hôtel-Restaurant Saint Antoine over there to the right, and the Hôtel Restaurant Petit Saint Benoît to the left.

All French commercial travellers agreed that Saint Antoine was unsurpassed for blue trout straight from the river. The mushroom omelette, too, was very good.

On the other hand, given reasonable notice, say a little half-hour or so, just the time to appreciate an apéritif and a pleasant chat, Petit Saint Benoît had a way of serving a Chicken Marengo to which even the most commercial kissed the tips of the fingers for ever after.

Jan, mightily oppressed by his advancing years, decided he definitely needed the apéritif, the pleasant chat, and the Chicken Marengo. So he crossed over to the Petit Saint Benoît.

He was not disappointed. A quarter of an hour later, he was enjoying the most interesting conversation with Madame the proprietor and a couple of gentlemen, obviously Madame's regular clients and sympathetic friends.

Madame was naturally enchanted to hear that this much-travelled gentleman had been wolfing down the kilometres ever since seven that morning so as to have the pleasure of celebrating his birthday with a peerless Chicken-Marengo-

Petit-Saint-Benoît. Before he attended to his lesser affairs in the town, naturally!

She was even more enchanted when Jan ordered a very special bottle and invited them all to help him to celebrate.

They did more. By the time Jan's coffee steamed on the table, Madame and her friends had given Jan the most valuable instructions on how to handle their important ironmonger.

On entering the shop, for instance, he was on no account to inquire jocularly why the devil the new gold letters on the window said: Ironmongery of the Rue Saint Louis, when the rusty notice nailed on the wall at the end of the street clearly stated that fifty years ago the name of the street had been changed to: Rue de la République.

Ah yes! He was to keep it well in mind that their important ironmonger was also a white-hot Royalist.

Indeed, in his opening gambit, he would do well to bring in Buckingham Palace of Great Britain, or maybe better still Holland of the Boer War days, when there was a queen on the throne who could, and did speak her mind most regally, and the back of her royal hand to all those who yelped that a reigning monarch—and a woman at that —had no divine right whatever to a conscience of her own.

More vital still, Jan was never to forget that in 1912 their important ironmonger had invested a whole pot of good French money in Ten per cent Imperial Russian Redeemables, guaranteed by all that was sacred in Holy Russia. But by 1920, of course, the Comrades were tying down their communal jam-pots with all that sort of bourgeois paper. So Jan was to strive to spit out flames of fury at the very mention of Soviet Russia.

Thus garlanded with much good counsel and a thousand good wishes, Jan shook hands all round; and feeling far, far younger, set out to interview Monsieur Gaston Pacoret of the Ironmongery of the Rue Saint Louis situated half way down the Rue de la République.

Now it may be true that "the help of good counsel setteth business straight", or it may have been the fine afterglow of the Chicken Marengo and the special bottle; but whatever it was, Jan sang the praises of his stoves that afternoon with so golden a tongue that Monsieur Pacoret was positively hypnotised into listening—always the most delicate part of any commercial interview. And presently, much to his own surprise, Monsieur Pacoret heard himself placing a cautious order, with a still more cautious promise of future favours, if this little consignment sold half as well as Jan and his leaflets so eloquently swore they would.

Moreover Jan walked out of that ironmongery with a genuine respect for Monsieur Pacoret. He had never seen a shop more admirably stocked, with everything so impeccably arranged from the buckets and brooms, coffee-mills and casseroles, to the watering-cans and egg-whisks.

Then there were Mesdemoiselles Victorine and Herminie, Monsieur Pacoret's sisters. Elderly they might be, at least fifteen years older than their brother, but how briskly they made out the bills, and how sensibly and amicably they advised the customers!

Yes, thought Jan, there was an atmosphere, a flavour, about the Ironmongery of the Rue Saint Louis . . . old-fashioned, reliable, precise, it was an establishment that one instinctively trusted and respected.

It reminded him of some other place, a place that now tugged at his memory, pleading to be recalled.

Dear Heaven above, yes! Now he had it!

And Jan strolled on, smiling to himself; and thinking for the first time in many years of our Oma's shop in Amsterdam.

Chapter XII

THE MAN OF THE WORLD

That year was an excellent one for the Ironmongery of the Rue Saint Louis, and for everyone else in that little town as well. The crops had done well; the vines had surpassed all expectations, so there was good money about—waiting to be sensibly invested, of course.

And Monsieur Pacoret was quick to note that Jan's handsome stoves suffered no dust to collect under their feet but speedily sold themselves in the most profitable way. But, naturally, he said nothing of this to Jan. Business is business—especially if it is good.

But as the months went by, his manner became more and more cordial, and he confided in his sisters that this tall Swede . . . or was he Dutch . . . anyway, it didn't matter . . . now, he was a good type. There was something sound and pleasant about *him* as well as his stoves. And the man talked sense, too. Yes, one now quite looked forward to his visits.

Mademoiselle Victorine and Mademoiselle Herminie not only agreed, they said Jan was also one of the few men one could trust to carry out a job. Look, for instance, how he had offered to take that new raincoat of Gaston's back to the shop in Paris; *and* stood over them, too, seeing to it that they dispatched the genuine article as advertised and illustrated in their autumn catalogue.

Oh yes, they were likeable and dependable, both Jan and his stoves.

Presently, Monsieur Pacoret began to invite Jan to step into the prim parlour behind the shop to discuss business, and take a little glass of something or a cup of coffee. And between customers, Mademoiselle Victorine or Mademoiselle Herminie would take it in turns to slip in and have a word with him as well. And Jan would sit on one of the hard stiff chairs, amiably talking of this and that, cracking little jokes, and answering questions—very conscious of the honour they were paying him, and more than a little flattered to sense they now considered him a most reliable authority on the untidy palpitating world outside, of which one liked to be intelligently informed even if one could not often approve.

Jan, obliging as ever, saw to it they were not disappointed. He even began to keep a secret Pacoret Notebook, in which he jotted down memos of anything that might safely be told in the parlour of the Ironmongery of the Rue Saint Louis, or which might come in handy down at the Café de la Mairie where Monsieur Pacoret enjoyed his nightly argument and game of cards. And where he was now beginning to enjoy a growing reputation for startling the company with such inside information as:

I tell you the Queen of Holland herself comes down the steps of her palace to greet this deputation of fishermen, and they present her with the first catch of the season—fine, fat young herrings so tender and sweet the Dutch swallow them raw.

And then bursting with vitamins they tear out and get on with pushing back the sea. That'll show you what raw herrings can do for a nation!

The English! But I tell you they've always believed in other people minding their own business. A friend of mine swears they have a tombstone over there that growls:

> *Reader, pass on, nor waste your time,*
> *On bad biography or bitter rhyme,*
> *For what I am, this humble dust ensures,*
> *And what I was, is no affair of yours.*

And the knowledgeable Monsieur Pacoret basking in the roars of applause that greeted these little triumphs would decide he really would present Jan with a half-bottle of his "fine Napoleon" when he called in at the New Year.

But when Jan breezed into the shop that January, he was firmly halted in the doorway by Mademoiselle Victorine.

"Monsieur," she said abruptly, "Gaston is in bed, ill. The influenza. But my sister and I would be obliged if you would be good enough to come back later on. We close at twelve sharp for lunch as you know. So will you look in about a quarter to one?"

"With pleasure, Mademoiselle," said Jan, and before he had time to ask a sympathetic question or two about Monsieur Pacoret, she had whisked round to attend to a waiting customer.

But there was something in the quick half-smile she gave him as she turned away that reassured Jan. He had done nothing to upset them. No, poor Mademoiselle Victorine was clearly very worried. About Monsieur Pacoret's influenza, of course. She and her sister loved the very ground he walked on.

At a quarter to one, then, there sat Jan in the neat parlour behind the ironmongery, accepting a cup of coffee from

Mademoiselle Victorine and a cigarette from Mademoiselle Herminie.

To his dismay, they both looked very tired and pale, and extremely worried.

"I do hope . . ." began Jan.

"No, Monsieur, no," said Mademoiselle Victorine, "Gaston is not worse. The doctor assures us it is nothing but a sharp attack of influenza. He will be up and about in a week or so. It is not that . . ."

She sighed heavily. So did Mademoiselle Herminie.

Jan cleared his throat, preparing to ask what calamity had then befallen them, when Mademoiselle Victorine spoke again.

"No, Monsieur, it is not Gaston's illness, worrying though that is . . ."

She faltered, and blew her nose.

"No," said Mademoiselle Herminie, "the truth is . . . we have been doing some serious thinking, my sister and I. Very serious indeed."

"Then suppose you tell me about it?" gently suggested Jan, hating to see them so distressed.

The genuine note of concern in his voice broke the ice. Out it all poured, and Jan listened without a word.

They were, as Jan must have remarked, considerably older than their brother. In fact, Mademoiselle Victorine was fifteen years older, and Mademoiselle Herminie was sixteen and a half older.

But so far, everything had gone quite smoothly and happily. Papa and Maman had left them the business between them. It kept all three of them very busy. So busy they never stopped to think seriously of the future—as one should . . . as one really should.

But this sudden illness of Gaston's, all the trotting up and down the stairs, the managing alone in the shop, all this had at last shaken them into thinking most seriously.

One must face facts. They were growing old. It was not this, however, that was worrying them so. It was the thought the terrible thought, that one day poor Gaston might be nailed to his bed, as he was now—ill and miserable. And downstairs only a housekeeper as unconcerned as you please, except about such things as her wages and her time off, of course. Not to mention a couple of indifferents, wasting their time out there in the shop as like as not.

No, no, it was their duty, their most solemn duty to provide for Gaston's future well-being, whilst there was still time.

Here, they paused. And looked hard at Jan.

"Well, if I can . . ." began Jan, and then broke off hurriedly. What exactly could he offer to do? What could anyone do?

So he began to assure them that they still had years and years before them. At the moment they were both tired, and no wonder. But even so, they would put youngsters of twenty to shame. Heavens above, Jan had yet to meet a young woman brisk and efficient enough to hold a candle to either of them.

They cut him short. They said one must also be honest— there was another, and completely different side to every problem. One also had one's duty towards oneself. They had both worked hard all their lives. And though they had not yet had the heart to mention it to poor Gaston, who would be absolutely lost without them, they really would like to take things more quietly now, far more quietly. In fact they would like to retire to a little villa they had some miles out in the country. They'd had it in the family for years. They always went there for the holidays even when Papa and Maman were alive. "Mon Repos" it was called. And well, now they felt the time had come to make it truly their repose.

And again they paused. And looked hard at Jan.

"Yes," said Mademoiselle Herminie quietly, as if answering Jan's unspoken thought. "We really must find a good wife for our dear Gaston."

It was the way she said "we" that froze Jan to his chair. Heaven only knew, he had been asked to help with some queer things in his time, and never turned a hair. Only too happy to oblige. And good for business, too. But this, well, this took his breath away, and no mistake.

He recovered in time to hear Mademoiselle Herminie earnestly explaining that there was no need to unsettle poor Gaston just yet, especially as there was nobody in the least suitable in their own small town. Oh, there was Madame the Widow Tissot, of course. She'd had her eye on Gaston for years; always in and out of the shop making ridiculous little purchases. But Gaston had no opinion whatever of her. She read the wrong newspapers. And was forever twittering away about the mythical days when she and her sisters were the belles of Vichy.

No, dear Gaston's wife would have to be carefully chosen; hand-picked, as it were. She must be of a sensible and serious age, between forty and forty-five, if possible. Gaston himself would be fifty next August.

She must know something about keeping accounts; and must definitely not be above lending a hand in the shop.

And above all, oh, above all . . . and here, their eyes filled with tears, she must be kind, and sympathetic to

Gaston's "ideas" and cherish him for the dear honest man he so truly was, God bless him!

Very moved indeed, they all three then drank a little glass of something warm and comforting and Mademoiselle Victorine rose to her feet, and said they really must open the shop now, or Gaston might think something was wrong. And they knew, of course, that Jan would treat all this as strictly confidential; that he would never, never breathe a word to Gaston. But now he knew what was in their hearts, could they, might they rely on Monsieur Jan to keep his eyes and ears open as he travelled about?

And Monsieur Jan, looking down on their earnest, anxious faces, took their hands in his, and swore, yes, oh yes, indeed! Of course he would!

This fine quixotic mood, however, basely fell from Jan as he walked slowly back to the Hôtel Petit Saint Benoît.

Now what had he let himself in for? What was this for a fine idea, and not even one of his own invention!

Stoves, bicycles, wrist-watches, perambulators, even domestic pets at a pinch, he would be only too glad to help to supply. One could always apologise, and offer to take back an unsatisfactory article. One could even offer to try again.

But a wife! And with all those qualifications! Where would he begin to look for such a paragon? He, who lived from one small commercial hotel to another! Talk about looking for a sunbeam in a cucumber!

His own fault, of course. All his own fault. Those two poor ladies imagined him to move in a fine cheerful world full of talented, first-rate people. It was the way he talked.

Too darned optimistic about everything and everyone; every goose he met the whitest and most genial of swans.

No, the next time he called at the Ironmongery of the Rue Saint Louis, he must for once have the moral courage to say, regretfully but firmly, that he had no suggestions whatever to make, except maybe a little petition to Saint Jude who enjoys a reputation for bringing off the improbable. Or so Mademoiselle Victorine herself had once assured him.

Besides, what was Monsieur Pacoret going to say to this fitting him up with a good, suitable wife? Of course, one never knew with the French. They often took the most realistic view of marriage. And oddly enough, very successful it often worked out, too!

All the same, Monsieur Pacoret was in a class apart—a fiercely independent little man with a great sense of dignity. Jan would hate to lose his regard. And the regular orders, too, of course.

Truly, grumbled Jan, one had to be one hundred per cent pure French to expect a man to undertake so delicate and perilous a commission. No, no, this was definitely a problem for Saint Jude, or some other patient saint who specialised in finding the needle in the most unlikely of hayricks.

But the trusting faces of Mademoiselle Victorine and Mademoiselle Herminie *would* keep bobbing up before him; and Jan walked into the Hôtel Petit Saint Benoît looking so harassed that Madame the proprietor anxiously inquired if he, too, felt this new variety of influenza creeping upon him; or was it this new government affecting his liver? And she reached for a bottle guaranteed to dispel the initial gloom of any pestilence.

All this, however, was as nothing compared to what lay in store for Jan's next visit to the Ironmongery of the Rue Saint Louis. All that morning, he had been carefully rehearsing what he would say to Mademoiselle Victorine and Mademoiselle Herminie the moment Monsieur Pacoret was safely out of the way.

But it was Monsieur Pacoret himself who met him in the doorway. And to Jan's surprise, he was wearing his shaggy goatskin coat, and wide, black felt hat.

"Ah!" he said. "Just the man I wanted to see. I'm on my way to the dentist. You might as well walk so far with me."

With these ominous words, he swept Jan back into the street again, and for a moment they paced along in grim silence.

Then Monsieur Pacoret spoke again.

"Monsieur," he said, "I will speak the truth. The dentist is not the real reason I am out. I saw you coming up the street, and I seized the chance to have a word with you . . . in private. We will go to the Café de la Mairie. It is always quiet there at this hour of the morning."

He led the way across the square and into the warm café; selected a secluded table, and called for drinks.

"Monsieur," said Monsieur Parcoret, very solemn and tense, "I am sure you have realised by now that my sisters and I regard you as a friend, a very real friend."

Jan began to say he was truly honoured but Monsieur Pacoret wasn't prepared to listen.

"And so," he hurried on, "I feel I may permit myself the liberty to say you are essentially a man of the world. Yes, yes, it stands out a mile. And this has decided me to ask for your advice on a matter of the utmost gravity. To tell the truth, there is no one here in whom I would wish to confide. You know how it is in a small town like this where one has lived all one's life. One instinctively builds a wall of privacy about one's real self."

Jan, very perplexed, but mightily relieved at the way the interview was going, said yes, indeed.

"So I will come straight to the point," went on Monsieur Pacoret. "But first I must ask you for your solemn word that you will never divulge any part of what I am going to tell you to my two sisters. They would feel mortally hurt. You know how devoted they are to me."

So Jan swore eternal silence, uneasily praying now that Monsieur Pacoret was not involved in some Royalist plot to hamstring the Republic.

"Yes, Monsieur," said Monsieur Pacoret, "I have two devoted sisters. No man could wish for better. But to tell the truth I am growing more and more worried about them. They are both getting on in years. And I feel they should be taking things more easily."

"Yes," said Jan, "I must say I thought they both looked very tired the last time I called."

"Ah!" said Monsieur, very satisfied indeed. "But how in the devil am I to suggest it is perhaps time they retired? No woman likes to be told to her face she is past her job."

Jan said no, it would have to be done very tactfully indeed. And then, of course . . .

"Yes, yes," rushed in Monsieur Pacoret, "I know precisely what you are about to say. They would worry about me. I am all the world to them."

Monsieur Pacoret suddenly shot up in his chair, and threw out imploring hands.

"Monsieur Jan," he said, "for the love of Heaven, advise me! Tell me how to break it to them!"

"I wish to get married!"

"Married, Monsieur Jan!"

"Now!" Jan heard himself say, as his head cleared a little. "What is this for a fine idea!"

"Thank you!" said Monsieur Pacoret, very moved indeed, and held out his hand. So they shook hands on the fine idea, and called for another drink.

Then Monsieur Pacoret carefully outlined the situation. He was thinking—absolutely honourably, of course—of a very serious and intelligent woman called Paulette Martin. She worked in the Bank of France in a neighbouring town where Monsieur Pacoret went every Thursday.

Nice-looking in a quiet way; dark eyes, and brown hair, now growing a little grey, and no wonder after years and years of a most responsible job, and nursing an invalid mother. Still a very trim figure, though.

And a remarkable head for accounts! Twenty-seven years in the Bank of France, and never a franc wrong, no matter what the rush.

Monsieur Pacoret had felt drawn to her for years. In fact some twenty years ago he had made a few discreet inquiries. One had to be sensible and realistic. But there was no hope, no hope at all. She had this invalid mother, and her strong sense of duty.

And Monsieur Pacoret had his two sisters, and *his* sense of duty.

Could Jan honestly imagine a happy household of four women and one man, all with a strong sense of duty? Jan truthfully said no, he couldn't. He simply couldn't.

But now, went on Monsieur Pacoret, things were altogether different. Paulette's mother had died very suddenly, on New Year's Day of all days, the poor soul. And last Thursday when Monsieur Pacoret had paid his weekly visit to the Bank of France, Paulette had quietly told him she was now thinking of packing up, and joining her brother in Algeria.

Yes, Algeria!

Very taken-aback, Monsieur Pacoret had stammered he hoped she was not taking so serious a step without giving it much careful thought.

And Paulette had looked him straight in the eyes, and her voice said:

"No, indeed, Monsieur! Of course not!"

But her eyes, oh, her eyes had said: "Tell me, what else is there for me to do? What else dare I hope?"

And when he had ventured to place his hand on hers, she, too, was trembling with emotion.

And then a whole crowd of people seemed to surge from nowhere, waving their infernal cheque-books. But the quick, warm smile she had given him as she turned away had made him walk deliciously on air . . . till he remembered his two sisters waiting for him, so devotedly, at home.

"Tell me," said Jan. "Have they ever met Mademoiselle Paulette?"

"No," said Monsieur Pacoret. "They simply don't know she exists. What was there to tell them, anyway? We have never said much more than good-day to each other."

"Listen," said Jan, "you take that walk to the dentist. You needn't go in, of course. Or go and take a look at the river. But whatever you do, give me at least an hour with your sisters. I may be able to arrange this little matter for you. No, no, don't worry! I'll keep my promise. I swear I shall never breathe a word of this conversation!"

And here Jan put on an air that he hoped was convincingly man of the world, and leaning across the table he said, very significantly, "With women, one has to be subtle, and delicately sympathetic. One must always allow them the innocent pleasure of thinking they are managing everything themselves."

"Ah!" breathed Monsieur Pacoret, very impressed. "But how . . ."

"Leave everything to me," said the man of the world. "Meet me here in exactly one hour."

An hour and a half later, a feverish Monsieur Pacoret greeted Jan.

"Well?" he implored. "Well?"

"Calm yourself," said Jan, and pulled up a chair.

"Now listen carefully. Whatever you do, show no undue interest if your sisters quietly manage to find a mutual friend to introduce them to Mademoiselle Paulette. And don't give yourself away if they invite her over to lunch one Sunday. Just agree, but not too enthusiastically, that she seems a very nice, sensible woman.

"After that, it should be plain sailing.

"But I beg of you, indeed I rely on you to allow them to go on having the unselfish pleasure of thinking they thought of this first; that they are arranging this marriage for you . . . in spite of yourself. Do I make myself clear?"

"Most beautifully clear," choked Monsieur Pacoret. And he jumped up from his chair, and embraced Jan on both cheeks.

Three months later, Monsieur Pacoret quietly married Mademoiselle Paulette Martin. And Mademoiselle Victorine and Mademoiselle Herminie retired to "Mon Repos" in a gentle glow of self-congratulation.

They presented Jan with a handsomely framed photograph of the Ironmongery of the Rue Saint Louis, with all four of them smiling in the doorway. And across one corner, in Mademoiselle Victorine's neat pointed handwriting, it said,

"With affection and gratitude."

And Jan, it seemed, had no qualms of conscience whatever about accepting all this, being of the opinion that one does not pull up something so harmless and gratifying by the roots—especially if one has nothing better to plant in its place.

Chapter XIII

BIRTHDAY IN HOLLAND, 1940

Six months later, Jan was working in Switzerland—
something to do with alarm-clocks this time. This job,
it seemed, had suddenly dropped from the sky,
together with a letter asking if Jan was interested.

Immediately, the old urge to travel on had surged up
in him, and by the end of the month he had taken an affectionate leave of all his friends in France, the sports car, and his
stoves; and was off to Geneva.

Jan knew, of course, that Tanta Joh would be most upset
to learn that he had handed in his notice yet once again—
and to so sensible a business-house, too. So he wrote her a
light-hearted letter, saying even the best of salesmen
couldn't go on selling stoves for ever, at least not that sort
of stove. The darn things were wellnigh fool-proof! They
lasted for ever! But alarm-clocks, now they were merrily
over-wound by the million every night of the week all over
the world.

He then agreed that it was indeed a pity he had never
been able to get down to Marseilles to visit Paul and Philippe
and their little families. But maybe he would be able to fit
in a trip from Geneva one of these days.

And Tanta Joh wasn't to lose any sleep over that Austrian
—Adolf Hitler. Sooner or later somebody would be bound

to crack him on the head with a beer-mug, or send him for a nice long walk to the pump.

And he was glad the garden was looking so nice, and here he was at the bottom of the page with just the room to send his best greetings to all, and to sign himself, their loving son, Jan.

Mynheer Vos, it appears, was very puzzled at the look on Tanta Joh's face as she read and re-read this reassuring letter.

"Well?" he asked. "What is wrong?"

Tanta Joh reluctantly admitted that there seemed to be nothing wrong. But all the same, she had the strangest feeling that Jan wasn't nearly so light-hearted as he was trying to sound. If he was, he would have dropped one of his cards—not bothered to write a whole letter.

"Dear Heaven above!" sighed Mynheer Vos. "You grumble away when he drops one of his cards, and now, when for once he takes the trouble to sit down and write a letter, you sit there looking as if he was inviting us all to his own funeral! Potvordikkie! There is no understanding any woman."

Jan was still in Switzerland when the Second World War came crashing about us, extinguishing all our last desperate hopes of peace.

And we were all very moved to receive telegrams from Geneva, urging us, if at all possible, to send our children over there to him. But we naturally wondered how on earth he would cope with a band of unknown children; and back from England, France and Holland went our telegrams, thanking him warmly, but saying we thought it best to keep our children home with us.

Besides, as Philippe wrote to me, so far this seemed to be a "drôle de guerre"—no wonder the Americans were talking of a "phoney war"—a few shells exchanged from time to time across the Rhine; loud-speakers blaring across No Man's Land; the British Air Force gently dropping leaflets over Germany; and the French Red Cross organising libraries for the bored troops in the Front Line.

And all the walls of Paris plastered with posters: Chantons quand même! Let's sing all the same!

Oh yes, for seven months it was a queer war all right, so queer that when Hitler suddenly stretched out his jackboots and trampled down Denmark and Norway, we were stricken with genuine surprise as well as horror. But as everybody was soon telling everybody else, this might be a "tactical success"; it was also an "enormous strategic error".

So, at the beginning of May, 1940, Jan had very little real difficulty in travelling back to Holland to be with his mother again on her birthday—the tenth of May, if you remember.

And Tanta Joh, it seemed, had faithfully promised her husband that for that day, at least, she would try not to worry about their other sons, all four now called up, two in the Dutch Army, two in their Air Force. Hadn't Hitler solemnly promised not to attack Holland as long as she remained neutral? Maybe, this time, he would keep a promise. In any case, Tanta Joh fully intended to keep hers.

And it seems she got up very early on her birthday, and went downstairs to get the breakfast, determinedly humming a little tune to herself as she went.

It was beautiful weather. One would imagine, thought Tanta Joh, as she put on the kettle, that the spring was trying to make up for the hard, bitter winter. The magnolia tree in the back garden was in full bloom. Jan was just in time to see it at its very best. It had never looked so lovely. And the polders all about the house looked beautiful, too. They positively shone with buttercups and daisies. Oh, a lovely, golden day for a birthday! If only . . .

She had just ground the coffee when something made her go to the window again.

In the meadow across the road, old Farmer Kost was sitting on a stool by the side of his black and white cow. But he wasn't milking her. His round, red face was turned up to the blue morning sky.

"Jan! Kees!" cried Tanta Joh, her heart suddenly hammering loudly within her. "Come here! What . . . is that?"

There, high in the sky, floated a thousand small white clouds. And as they stared, they heard a monstrous thud-thudding, and all the windows rattled and shook. And down from the peaceful Dutch sky floated those white clouds, each with a grotesque doll dangling from it.

And, oh dear God, they were no dolls, but paratroops, armed to the teeth!

Ten terrible minutes later, old Farmer Kost lay dead in his field, but the cow grazed on. And six of the paratroopers had kicked in Tanta Joh's door, each holding a pistol in one hand, the other on the grenades ready in his belt. And they were nothing but boys, arrogant boys of eighteen or nineteen at the most.

But they knew what they had to do. They locked Tanta Joh and her husband in the cellar, but they made Jan march up the stairs before them, hands above his head.

"Try any tricks in that cellar," they rapped, "and we put a bullet through this fellow's head."

Within the hour, they had turned Tanta Joh's neat little

house into a small fortress. Machine-guns jutted from the gaping holes where once shone her clean windows. And the trim little curtains, washed and ironed to welcome Jan, lay in a crumpled heap beneath the magnolia tree.

It was almost dark when Jan came running down to let them out of the cellar.

"They've gone," he said. "Another of them came racing up on a motor-bike with orders to retreat."

And when Tanta Joh went into her sitting-room, her furniture, her beloved, polished furniture, lay in wanton ruin. And she took a brush and pan and began to sweep up the glass. But the tears that ran down her face were not for her ruined furniture. No, no! Yesterday, all that mattered. But not now! Not now!

Well, if you remember, the invasion of Holland lasted five days, five black days.

But the blackest of them all for my Tanta Joh was the day they switched on the radio and heard a Dutch voice quietly talking, in German, to Germany.

"During the First World War," said the voice, "we Dutch raised large loans so that we might send food to starving German children, whom we rightly regarded as innocent victims of war. When that war came to an end, we did more. We welcomed tens of thousands of these children into our homes. They came to us in relays, one after another. We gave them the best food in our land to fight their rickets, their tuberculosis. Tens of thousands of Dutch homes took unto themselves German boys, and cared for them as their sons, sending them home well and strong.

"Now, these boys, grown into men, have returned to Holland . . . to kill . . . to destroy . . ."

Jan got up and switched off. His face was grey.

"I was one of those boys," he said. "I was one of them."

And before Tanta Joh could find words to answer his grief, there was a loud knocking at the door. No Germans this time, but the Dutch police—to arrest Jan.

"You are German by birth," they said. And it was no use protesting that Jan left Germany when he was but a lad, that he hardly remembered his German father; that his mother and stepfather were Dutch; that they, and all the rest of our family, would stake their lives that he was no traitor to Holland. Orders were orders. All Germans were to be put safely under lock and key. And quite right, too. Every man, woman and child of them seemed to have orders from Hitler to make as much trouble as possible. And they handcuffed Jan, marched him to a waiting car, and drove off in the direction of Rotterdam.

This was about midday, May 14th. At half past one the Germans bombed Rotterdam. There were no balloons, no anti-aircraft guns, no defences of any kind. And no air-raid shelters. But there was a wind, an infernal wind, that sent the flames leaping and roaring from house to house, from avenue to avenue.

All that afternoon the smoke poured up from the blazing city, and Tanta Joh knelt and prayed in her shattered home.

As night fell, they heard a car drive up in the silence outside.

"Open the door, Mutti," croaked a voice. "Don't be afraid!"

Mutti! It must be Jan! Only Jan called her Mutti. Tanta Joh flew to open the door. Out there, in the darkness, two men were leaning from a car.

"We can't wait," one said. "Take care of him."

Then the darkness swallowed them up; and along the garden path staggered a man, and pitched forward across the step on his face.

And when Tanta Joh knelt to look, it *was* Jan. And oh, his feet, his hands, were most pitiful to see.

He had been taken to the jail in Rotterdam; and that had caught fire, too. And the jailers had come racing round, unlocking and opening all the doors, before they and all the prisoners had fled into the burning streets.

They had taken away Jan's shoes, so he ran in his felt slippers. And presently they were smouldering on his feet, so he tore them off, and ran in his socks, on, on, till a car came plunging through the smoke, and drew up to give him a lift.

By the time Jan was limping round again, it was all over. The whole of Holland was occupied by the Nazis. Every Dutch plane had been lost, and with them two of Jan's step-brothers. The other two were prisoners of war.

With smooth, sinister efficiency the Nazis took over, helped by many a German who had been making a comfortable living in Holland. And helped too, ironically enough, by Dutch love of order itself.

Every year the Dutch Central Office for Statistics proudly published an impressive book in which was set down exactly how much coal was hewed, how much beer was brewed, and everything else about Holland that could be told in figures. This mine of information was, of course, a positive gift to the Nazis, a fine "catalogue for plundering" as somebody bitterly put it, which also obligingly told them precisely where to lay hands on everything listed therein.

And all the while the radio was blaring away, explaining that Adolf Hitler was determined to see that Holland had a place in the sun in his New European Order, that the Nazis were there as protectors and friends. Till one day, it abruptly changed its tune, and began warning the obstinate Dutch that even Hitler's patience might wear thin if they continued to be as deaf as posts, and so dourly unco-operative.

Then one day, Jan went off to Amsterdam, on a little business-trip, he told Tanta Joh. And late that evening he was sitting outside a café, when two men sat down at a nearby table. It was almost dark, and Jan took them to be tram-conductors.

Now the tram-conductors of Amsterdam have a reputation all their own. They have a broad and hearty sense of humour, and are as quick to laugh as to swear. But these two seemed in the very sourest of moods. And after speaking their minds about the beer, one of them began to abuse the Queen.

"Deserted us!" he shouted, and banged his fist on the table. "Took all our gold! Left us in the lurch! Gone to live in comfort in Buckingham Palace!"

Jan put down his glass and rose to his feet.

"Use your thick head," he said. "What use would she be to us *here*?"

And then saw, too late, that they were not tram-conductors. They were wearing the uniform of the Lonely Ones, the Dutch Nazis. Yes, that is what they called themselves— and with reason—the Lonely Ones.

And these two Lonely Ones bawled to a policeman just coming off traffic-duty, and ordered him to arrest Jan.

The policeman gave one look at them, and then at Jan;

and promptly obeyed. But as they crossed the first bridge, the policeman muttered, "I get fainting-fits. I've got a proper doctor's certificate to prove it. So I'm going to faint right here and now. And the moment I collapse, for God's sake, step on it."

So Jan stepped in it . . . into the safe darkness.

The following morning Tanta Joh came downstairs and saw a letter lying on the mat. Somebody must have pushed it under the front door.

Best of Parents,

Forgive me if I leave you like this, with no word of warning. The truth is—I have once again found a new job that looks interesting.

If you are asked where I am, speak the simple truth— you do not know.

Try not to worry. The future is always nearer than we think. In fact, I am hoping to help it along a little.

Mutti, if ever I have to go away on a long trip, I promise you I will call in to kiss you before I go. So don't worry if you do not hear from me.

Well, God bless you both,

Your loving son, JAN.

PS. Burn this at once please.

Tanta Joh read this aloud to her husband—then they looked at each other in silence.

"Ja, Kees!" said Tanta Joh, answering his unspoken thought. "Ja! Our Jan is up to something!"

And she tore the letter and the envelope into tiny pieces, and carefully burnt them in the stove.

Chapter XIV

TRAPPED

Years ago, during that winter holiday I once spent in Holland, Oma and I were invited to spend a day with old friends of hers in Rotterdam. They lived in one of a long line of tall, narrow houses along the bank of a canal. And they took me up to the attic, flung open a small window, and said, "There! How's that for a fine view!"

I leaned out, and I remember how odd it seemed to me to see the masts of ships moving among the housetops and the tall trees. But oddest of all to my eyes, there, in the centre of that great busy port, stood a windmill as tall as a steeple, peacefully turning its sails against the soft, grey sky.

Now on the morning when Tanta Joh found that letter on her doormat, Jan made his way to this very windmill. Yes, there it still stood. By some miracle, it had escaped the flames, the bombs. And it is an old custom of Dutch millers to tell the world how they are feeling by the way they set the sails of their mills. And Jan, looking up at that gaunt, blackened mill, saw that its sails were set in the position that means sorrow, deep mourning.

He stood there for a moment; and then picked his way through the rubble to a group of men clearing the foundations of some great building. One of them watched him come and then waved to a large notice:

Trapped
Spectators and Talkers
Are not welcome.
Either go Home or
OFFER TO LEND A HAND.

Jan nodded, and then pulled a door-key from his pocket and held it out.

The man put down his spade.

"So you've come," he said. "But I warn you, I'm not the only one who thinks we are taking a risk with you."

"So I understand," said Jan. "It has taken me weeks to talk my way this far. Now where do I go?"

"You'll see," said the man, and pulled on his coat. "Come on!"

That evening, my cousin Jan started on his new job—making keys, in a cellar in a back street of Amsterdam. Yes, keys. It was one of the trades he had picked up as he knocked round the world.

And the workers in the Dutch Underground Movement were soon finding Jan's keys very useful indeed. With them they opened safes in Food Offices and helped themselves to yard upon yard of coupons for bread and the other food they needed to feed many an Allied airman who had baled out over Holland, and now lay hidden—until Jan and other experts were able to cut the keys that would open the safes that would provide them with identity cards and other necessary papers.

But maybe the keys Jan most enjoyed making were those that opened the filing-cabinets that held the names and addresses of many an unhappy Jew, and other suspected persons, due to be dealt with by the Nazis.

Then there were the keys to fit the filing-cabinets in

which were stored the records and whereabouts of distinguished cows and pigs. It did something to Dutch blood-pressure to see photographs of their pedigree stock in the newspapers, and to read:

> *Healthy, high-valued cows, presented by*
> *the Dutch to Adolf Hitler, with thanks*
> *for protection received.*

Yes, what with one key and another, Jan was kept very busy in his cellar.

Then presently, when it was realised that this German-Dutchman could be trusted, a small printing-press was set up in his cellar. And on this, Jan began to turn our hundreds of leaflets in German, the latest B.B.C. news-bulletins, which the Nazis would find among their letters, or in their pockets of a morning, or pasted on the wind-screens of their cars.

Then, by way of a change, he would turn out leaflets in Dutch that sent ripples of laughter all over Holland, all the latest Underground jokes, especially his two favourites:

> *Lady, arrested for listening to B.B.C.: But of course*
> *I was! Adolf Hitler said he was going to speak from*
> *Broadcasting House in London this October. You*
> *wouldn't want me to miss it, would you?*

And:

> *The Dutch Nazis are on parade. All passers-by have been*
> *ordered to stop and watch them. As they march past, one old*
> *man begins to shout greetings: "Hello, Dirk! How goes it, Piet?*
> *Well, fancy seeing you, Klaas!"*
>
> *Then he turns to the silent, glowering crowd, and brags: "Yes,*
> *I know them, every single one. I'm a retired jailer, you see!"*

And it seemed that one earnest young Dutchman almost reproved Jan.

"I may be wrong," he said, "but I have the strongest feeling that you want to make everyone laugh—even the Moffen!"

"M'm!" said Jan. "Could be! It's a language everybody understands, you know."

As time went on, Jan became more and more useful, especially when it was discovered that he also spoke and understood English. And presently he was promoted from his cellar to a small room high up in a great block of flats. But where that room was, and what he did there, nobody will ever know. There are some things that are not disclosed, even to-day.

Now it had been decided that Jan was to keep all his papers: birth-certificate, identity card, passport, and so on. It was felt that they might come in useful one day. They did.

One dark evening he was crossing a bridge, when he was pounced upon by the S.D. men. The S.D. men were the Sicherheits Dienst, the State Safety Service, but more accurately known as the Man Hunters.

A Nazi officer had just been found floating in the waters under that bridge, and this time the S.D. were going to act smartly. They were going to shoot every man and boy within so many yards of the crime.

But as they ordered Jan to stand with his face to the wall, he coolly refused.

"Take a look at my papers, you fools!"

And such was the arrogant note in his voice, that they stopped to examine his papers. And then marched him off to Headquarters to make sure he was indeed a good German.

"Why haven't you reported here before?" barked an officer. "Haven't you seen the posters? Don't you read the newspapers? Why do you think regulations are published, tell me that!"

"It's like this, Herr Hauptmann," said Jan, putting on the act of his life. "Germans are not popular round here . . . and after all the trouble we've taken to protect them from the British, too . . . And the minute I open my mouth, they know I'm a German. So I hardly ever go out. That's why I'm such a bad colour. And I have to take such care of my health, and my eyes are so bad. And I'm well over forty, so what use am I to the Fatherland?"

"Leave us to decide that," rapped the officer. "Report back here at nine sharp to-morrow morning for a medical examination. No, no, we'll take care of your papers."

And as Jan went through the door, he added, very casually, "I should turn up if I were you. We have our own way of dealing with the families of deserters."

But at nine sharp next morning, it was a Dutch doctor who was interviewing that officer. He said he was just about to go to bed the night before, when he heard a man groaning and calling for help in the darkness outside. He had, of course, gone out to see what was wrong, and there lay my cousin Jan. He had tripped over something, fallen down a flight of stone steps, and broken his right leg and arm.

"Leg AND arm!" snarled the officer.

"It was the way he fell," explained the doctor. "He's a heavy man, and he needs spectacles. His sight is bad."

"So he mentioned," agreed the officer, tapping a pencil on the desk, and looking hard at the doctor.

"Well, what am I to do with him?" asked the doctor.

"He's now on a couch in my waiting-room, but I can't keep him there, of course."

"You'll keep him where we think fit. What's the address?"

An hour later a German military doctor arrived at that Dutch doctor's house to examine Jan. He was a tired-looking man, about Jan's own age. And as he drew the blanket back over Jan's legs, he said, almost as if speaking to himself, "I was at the Russian Front last winter."

Jan looked at him. Neither of them spoke for a moment.

"My eyes play tricks," began Jan, "and in this cursed blackout . . ."

"Ja! Ja!" said the doctor. "Just stick to your story. I'll do what I can."

And he turned, and went wearily from the room.

But the S.D. man-hunters were taking no chances. That afternoon a German ambulance carried Jan off to have his right arm and leg X-rayed.

But that Dutch doctor was a specialist. He knew how to break bones so that even the most suspicious of German radiologists could not swear it was a put-up job.

And presently the ambulance carried Jan back again, fuming most artistically.

"Well, that'll do you for a time," said the Dutch doctor. "Later on, I'll think up a few normal complications. I only wish I could train you to be a convincing epileptic, or fit you up with one of my first-class duodenal ulcers, but I fancy I've arranged one too many of those already. I don't relish the way they're beginning to tap their pencils at me."

"There's my eyesight," suggested Jan.

"There are also good spectacles," said the doctor. "They'd rope in the blind now, if they had the chance. But don't worry. We'll think of something or the other to keep you out of their Victorious Army."

But for eight long weeks Jan lay in that Dutch doctor's waiting-room and worried. They had all his papers down there at Headquarters. By this time, they had undoubtedly traced his mother, his step-father, his two step-brothers, and our Dutch cousins.

And he couldn't allow the doctor to go on risking his neck for him.

Then he knew that it would not be considered safe to allow him to return to work. He was a marked man. From now on, he must pass his comrades in the streets and give no flicker of recognition. At all costs he must live up to his story. He was a lonely irritable German, with no friends, and very bad eyesight.

It seems that one thing and one thing alone cheered up those dark days. At half-past eight every Thursday evening the doctor and Jan would close the heavy shutters, and bar and bolt the door of the dispensary. Then they would take off the top of the sink in which the bottles were washed, and bring out a small portable radio-set. They would tune in to a raucous voice ranting away from the Ministry for Enlightenment of the Dutch People; and gradually slip over, turning down the volume as they went, to London . . . and Tommy Handley.

Yes, our Tommy Handley. They had to keep the volume so low that they missed half the jokes. But they could hear the laughter—the sane, homely, beautiful laughter. God must still be in His heaven, if men and women still laughed like that, so merry and kind.

And by and by, they would be laughing, too, till the tears ran down their faces. And when the show was over, the doctor would fetch out a precious bottle, and they would treat themselves to a tiny glass.

And standing to attention, they would lift their glasses and drink "To that man again!"

Now, for the sake of appearances, the doctor would sometimes ring up Headquarters and ask when they intended to take this German patient off his hands. And that, as calculated, always brought the reply that the patient would stay where he was till Authority saw fit to remove him. Meanwhile the doctor was responsible for his safety.

But one day, another German doctor was sent to examine Jan, a much younger man.

Unfortunately, Jan opened the door to him.

"Good!" he said. "Walking quite well without a stick I see. Excellent!"

That was a Friday.

The following Friday, my cousin Jan stepped on a tram from the Dam, the great square that lies before the Queen's Palace in Amsterdam.

Instantly, every passenger, men, women, even children, looked at him, then looked away again. But in their eyes he had seen something he had never seen before, never met before, in all his life.

Hatred. Cold, bitter hatred.

And suddenly a cold sweat broke out on his forehead, and he realised that from now on, wherever he looked, he would see it. For now he was in uniform—Hitler's uniform.

And for him there could be no escape. There was that paper they had made him sign, a paper which stated that in the event of his desertion, his whole family: his mother, his stepfather, his two step-brothers, our three Dutch cousins and their families, would all be sent to Labour Camps in Germany—or Poland. In plain words, to their deaths.

And he jumped from the tram, and sat down outside a café and called for a hot drink. It was a warm day, but he was shivering.

And he saw it again, in the face of the woman who served him, the two men who got up as he sat down, and walked away, leaving their drinks half-finished. Hatred. Hatred.

And a sudden fury shook him. He wanted to shout, "Blast you! Blast you! Can't you see I am still the same! Under this uniform, I am still the same!"

Then his rage fell from him. And he saw with bitter clarity that no good ever came of beating one's angry head against a stone wall of hate. Better accept it. He was trapped. Trapped. As others were trapped, God alone knew how many. That German doctor, for instance, the one who had said, "I was at the Russian Front." And he saw again the look in that doctor's eyes.

And suddenly a queer compassion choked him, as if a great prayer was welling up from deep inside him.

"Lord God," prayed my cousin Jan. "Take pity on us all, those who hate, and those who are hated."

And he got up, and walked the rest of the way to the station. He was going to keep his promise. He was going to kiss his mother before he went on a long trip.

One of his step-brothers opened the door.

"Ja?" he said. "Ja?"

And there it was again on his brother's face.

"So you don't recognise me in this rig-out?" asked Jan.

But now his mother came hurrying out.

"There's nothing wrong, is there?" she began.

Then she saw him there, standing on the step. But she didn't see the trappings, the uniform. No, no.

"Jan!" she cried, and held out both her arms.

"Come in, my son, come in!"

Chapter XV

THE WATERFALL

For the next two years, my Cousin Jan, now a private in the German Occupation Forces, was sent from place to place all over Occupied Europe. He even had one brief stay in Paris.

But no matter where he went, he always took infinite pains never on any account to earn any stripes. Indeed his artistic stupidity won him a considerable reputation even in his own company which was largely made up of men like himself—middle-aged conscripts of mixed parentage, hardly a man among them one hundred per cent pure German. They were, therefore, not to be trusted with any vital job for the Fatherland, and even in the humdrum duties with which they had to be trusted, it was notorious how often things went wrong—not to mention the exasperatingly high rate of suicides among them.

A slow, dull-witted lot . . . they couldn't even carry out a "razzia" efficiently. And Heaven knew a razzia was simple enough. All they had to do was swoop down on so many streets, block them off, and then march along each one in turn—looking for somebody on a bicycle. Then they shouted to him or her to get off. And confiscated the bicycle. It was as easy as that.

And I sometimes wonder what certain Parisian cyclists must have made of a six-foot burly Boche who fixed his steel spectacles on his nose as they rode into sight, and grumbled in fluent French, "Ah no! I told that sacred doctor these spectacles were no damn use. So kindly disappear before I *have* to see you. No, no, not that way! There's a type down there who's scared to death of all corporals. Allez! Allez! Fichez-moi le camp!"

Jan's company did not remain long in Paris. Even under an Occupation the Parisians are swift to exercise their caustic gift for mockery. And Authority, very touchy, sensed that these clod-hopping half-Germans were fast becoming figures of fun. So they were moved on to Caen.

Caen . . . where Monique Bobet had once whirled me along to see the great bicycle race, the Tour de France. And there, among all the uproar and excitement, we had come across Jan—Monsieur-my-Cousin-fallen-from-the-skies —and his two gay young companions.

And Jan found the restaurant, the very restaurant where we had eaten our merry meal that night. It was still open; and he sat down outside to drink a glass of cider.

And as he sat there, the long years rolled back, and he saw us again, under those very plane trees, all in our shining twenties, not caring a hoot who was Dutch, German, French or English. We were young, carefree, confident. Life was everything that was kind and merry. Dear Lord, how we had talked and laughed! Dear Lord, how happy we were!

Presently he was aware that a woman was staring at him, slumped there on his hard iron chair, so lost in thought. And he smiled, half apologetically.

And instantly met with a fierce, bitter look of contempt.

Ah well, it served him right. In that uniform, he ought to have known better than to smile, uninvited, at any human being. It was only at moments like this, when he was off his guard, that the misery of it all still caught him by the throat. Maybe old Frantz from Alsace was right, one never grew numb, indifferent . . . till one put a bullet through one's head.

Then he noticed that the woman, and the old man with her, were both in deep mourning. There were bands of crêpe round their arms.

And he got up, and walked away.

From Caen, Jan was sent to a small town in central France, a pleasant sunny place set among vineyards. Some miles to the south rose a high range of hills, thick with forests, and honeycombed with caves. And somewhere in those caves in the forests was the hide-out of the local Maquis—the French Resistance Movement.

Not that Jan's company was sent there to hunt down the Maquis. That was a job for skilled, efficient, young man-hunters, trained by the Gestapo. These middle-aged clod-hoppers were there to guard a couple of factories turning out spare parts for tanks, and the gas-works.

Now one warm spring night Jan was on guard outside his share of the gas-works when he heard the distant crack of a revolver. And presently a woman came running towards him. He could hear her panting. Behind her came the sound of voices.

Swift as thought, Jan caught the woman by the arm as she sped past, put one hand over her mouth, and fairly threw her into the dark gateway behind him.

"Don't breathe," he said, "or we'll both need coffins."

He shot back just in time. Two men were now racing down the road. They were civilians; but Jan saw the revolvers.

"The woman," said one in halting German. "Did you see her? Which way did she go?"

"Plaît-il?" said Jan. "Speak French, Monsieur. I'd understand better. Far better."

"The woman," rapped the man. "Did you see a woman?"

"But yes! Of course!" said Jan. "Running like a hare."

"Then, name of a name, why didn't you grab her?"

"Listen, Monsieur," said Jan. "The last time I grabbed a French woman she clouted me with her handbag, the lover she was bolting from stuck a knife in me, and I spent three months in the cooler. No, no, I don't grab any more Frenchwomen, not without orders."

"Oh, don't waste time on the fool," snarled the other. "Did you at least see which way she ran?"

"Straight on, I suppose," said Jan. "I hardly saw her, she ran so fast."

They tore on. Jan waited till the long road lay still and silent again. Then, without turning his head, he muttered:

"Now! What have you been up to? Those gentlemen were French!"

"French!" The woman almost spat. "They have forgotten that. They are sold body and soul to the Gestapo."

"Gestapo!" said Jan. "In that case you'd better slip out and run for it. If I know anything about them, they'll be doubling back soon with reinforcements."

The woman made no move.

"For God's sake," said Jan. "Hurry!"

Then he saw that she was there in the darkness, close beside him.

"Listen," she whispered. "I never thought I would say this again to any German. But I'll say it. Thank you!"

Then the miracle happened. He saw her dark eyes grow warm, grateful. And she smiled. She smiled! And disappeared into the night.

But that wasn't the end of the miracle. There was a lovely park in that small town. A little stream ran through it, and in one quiet corner it splashed and tumbled in a waterfall over some mossy rocks. Jan used to like to sit on a bench near this waterfall. Sometimes there would be children playing there, but if he pretended to be reading a newspaper they took no notice of him.

The following evening Jan made his way to this bench and sank down thankfully. His feet were troubling him. There were no children playing around, not a soul anywhere. So he took off his steel spectacles, and began to read his newspaper.

Suddenly, something made him look up. There, at the other end of the long bench, sat a woman. She was reading a newspaper, too. But now she raised her head and looked him straight in the eyes. Jan's heart missed a beat. But he held up his newspaper and spoke into it.

"So you're safe!" he said. "No, no, don't turn your head. Nobody can hear us with this noise of water, but there may be somebody watching. Never do for you to be seen talking to a German, of course."

"No," she said. "No."

"You will find it hard to believe," said Jan, turning over a page and scanning the advertisements, "but until I had to get into this uniform, I was doing . . . well . . . the same sort of job as you are, I imagine."

"Where?" she said. "Where?"

"In Holland. I am half Dutch."

She didn't speak, but Jan sensed her suspicion.

"Oh, I know what you are thinking," he said. "This may be a neat little trick to win your confidence. Listen, I have cousins here, in France, men of my own age. They're half Dutch, too. And I'd like *you* to do *me* a little favour now. As they say in English, one good turn deserves another. I'd like you to write them. Tell them their Cousin Jan had to get into this uniform or see all the family in Holland taken to Labour Camps. Tell them that. They will understand."

She half turned. Then bent over her paper again.

"But why ask me to do this?" she asked. "Why ask me?"

"I don't know," said Jan. "All I know is that I want you to believe me. And I can think of no other way. It is a good feeling to be believed."

She made no reply. And for a long time, they sat there in silence. Presently, it grew dusk, and there was no need to go on pretending to read newspapers. They were two shadowy figures, one each end of a long bench. And then it was night, and over there the waterfall sang endlessly in the warm darkness.

Jan was the first to speak.

"I like this place," he said.

"I love it," she said. "I played here as a child. It seems a long time ago, now."

She spoke as softly as before, but now her voice was different—as if all suspicion and misgiving had fallen from her. And Jan longed to move nearer, but dared not, for fear the warmth froze in that quiet voice.

"I had the slapping of my life on this very bench," she said presently, almost as if speaking to herself.

"My father died when my brother was still a baby. My mother had to work very hard. Lingerie. Beautiful things.

All by hand. I've known her sew right through a day and all through the night to finish an order in time.

"And when I wasn't in school, and of course every day of the holidays, I had to mind the baby.

"Poor Totor! He was always so pale, almost green. And always a cold in the nose. Always a cold!

"So my mother scraped up the money to take him to the doctor.

"'Madame,' he said, 'all this child needs is fresh air and sunshine.'

"'But, mon Dieu, he's out all day long!' screamed my mother. 'Out in the park with his sister here!'

"'That's all the medicine he needs,' insisted the doctor.

"So one afternoon, my poor Maman, still very worried, threw down her work, and came out to have a look at us enjoying the fresh air and sunshine.

"And there I was, brown as a nut, playing shops on this very bench.

"But the baby! Do you know where he was?

"Behind that waterfall! Yes, yes, behind the waterfall! There is a little grotto there with ferns as long as your arm, and very dark and damp, of course. And I used to make one dash with the pram, I hardly got wet, and leave him there, in the grotto, nice and safe, whilst I got on with my game.

"You should have heard my poor Maman!"

She gave a little laugh. And Jan longed to say, "Please go on. Please go on talking." But he didn't. Too afraid to shatter the spell.

Then the moon swam out in the dark sky. And she said abruptly, "These cousins of yours? What are their names; where do they live?"

Jan told her. And without another word, she got up and

walked quickly away. And in the moonlight, for the first time, Jan saw her clearly—a trim little woman in her middle thirties. And to Jan she was beautiful, most beautiful.

And he sat on in the darkness; and for the first time in many months his heart was soft and gentle within him. She had smiled at him . . . talked to him . . .

All that week, and all the next, Jan spent every free moment on that bench near the waterfall. But day after day dragged by, and there was no sign of her.

Then on the following Sunday, as he turned into the park, he saw her again, walking towards him with another woman. She gave no sign of recognition, but as they passed him he looked at her brown hands. There were no rings on them, not one.

And he heard her say, "Yes, at the Café de la Gare! But one must ask for it by name: Ouwe Klare, not Tip van Bootz!"

They both laughed. But Jan knew her words were meant for him. Ouwe Klare and Tip van Bootz are Dutch names for two well-known brands of Dutch gin. Nothing could be more Dutch.

And he turned and made for the Café de la Gare, and sat down on a chair on the pavement outside.

"Ouwe Klare," he said to the waiter who came out to serve him. "Not Tip van Bootz."

"Through there," said the waiter, "You'll find it on the right," and he waved as if directing Jan to the telephone or toilette.

So Jan went through the café, and as he turned to the right, a man standing there hustled him through a door and slammed and locked it behind them.

At a long table sat three men, a bottle and glasses before them.

"Sit down," said one of them. And there was nothing in his voice, no enmity, no friendship, no suspicion . . . nothing.

"We will waste no time. You claim to be first cousin to Philippe Jansen of Marseilles."

"And his brother, Paul," put in Jan.

"Paul Jansen," said the man, "died in a concentration camp three months ago. Don't you write to these cousins of yours?"

"In this uniform?" said Jan. "It would only embarrass them."

"Then maybe you can tell us . . ." began the man.

And for one long hour, on and on went the questions . . . how, when, where, why.

Then one of the men offered Jan a cigarette.

"We have to take infinite precautions," he said. "We have had to deal with others as word-perfect as you . . . and who also had names and addresses.

"By the way," he went on, his voice now very casual, "did you ever discuss sport with these French cousins of yours?"

"Sport?" echoed Jan.

"Yes . . . racing, wrestling, or fencing, for instance?"

"Good lord, yes!" said Jan. "Now I know what you're driving at! We used to practise old French boxing in a park in Amsterdam. And before we went to bed of a night, too, till our grandmother put her foot down. She said she wasn't going to have us kicking and punching her ceilings down."

The man made no comment, but began to unbutton the flap of his coat pocket. And he took out something and placed it quietly on the table.

"Does this mean anything to you?" he asked.

There, on the table, lay a little whistle.

"Yes," said Jan, his throat suddenly tight and dry. "Yes, if there is a figure nine scratched on it."

"Nine?" asked the man. "Why nine?"

"Our Dutch grandmother had nine grandchildren. And you know what kids are. I bought nine whistles; one each. Sort of secret family badge."

Nobody spoke for a moment. Then the man took the bottle, and filled four glasses.

And he rose to his feet, and said, "Gentlemen, we will drink to my Cousin Jan!"

Chapter XVI

OPERATION DESERTER

Yes, it was our Cousin Philippe! He had been brought up from Marseilles to question the German soldier claiming to be his cousin Jan.

It was absolutely imperative to discover what lay behind the curious behaviour of this German. Paul Jansen had lost his life through some devious treachery not yet tracked down. And now here was this man making free with the name and address of Philippe, who was also a key-worker in the Resistance Movement.

If he proved to be yet another ingenious decoy, he would have to be dealt with. And Philippe would forthwith disappear from the address in Marseilles.

If, on the other hand—and this was considered most unlikely—if it really was Jan Bauer, late of the Dutch Underground, who had so readily risked his neck to save one of them, then they would shake hands with this unusual comrade. But that was all.

All. They made that quite clear. In that uniform, in that small garrison town, there could be no question of anything else.

And Jan had not worked in his cellar in Amsterdam for nothing. He knew he was expected to ask no questions ... not even her name. Above all, he was expected never to risk seeking to see her again.

So he drank up his Ouwe Klare, shook hands all round, and got up to go.

And as he went, Philippe shook him again by the hand.

"Jan," he said. "My poor old Jan! When all this is over, write! Don't let us wait another thirty years to meet."

"No," said Jan. "No."

Two hours later, our Cousin Jan was on guard outside the gas-works again, staring down the long, silent road, wondering if he had been caught up in a dream.

Now this was the early summer of 1943.

Spring, 1944, found Jan in another unimportant French town in the valley of the Moselle in Lorraine.

Oddly enough, it was a Monsieur Karl Smit of Luxembourg who was to tell me something of what happened there. Monsieur Smit came to London on business some months after the end of the war, and Jan had given him our address. He was a quiet, middle-aged man with humorous grey eyes. We liked him from the start.

And one evening he said:

"You know perhaps that I was in France with your cousin all through the war, no?

"Oh yes, I was in the same company. My family have lived in Luxembourg for generations, but the Nazis discovered that my paternal grandfather was German. So they employed their usual persuasive arguments—I have a wife and three daughters all of an age to be of use in a Labour Camp. And well, soon, there I was in their Occupation Force in France. With Jan. We soon became friends.

"Now when we were in that little town in Lorraine, Jan and I used to drink a glass of wine of an evening in a small café—a dismal hole of a place, in a back-street. But it was quiet there—outside, I mean. We never went inside. We always sat outside. But even so, the woman who was serving us, was not precisely welcoming us. Ah no!

"However, one evening there was such a bitter wind that we picked up our glasses and walked inside.

"Instantly, four types playing cards pushed back their chairs and walked out. Now there were only Jan and I; and the woman, black as Hell, glowering behind her zinc bar.

"And at the sight of her face a great rage suffocated me.

"'Madame,' I said to her, 'Madame, you will, of course, find it most inconvenient to believe me. But we are not in your blasted country by choice. My companion here is half-Dutch. And I am from Luxembourg. And for both of us it was either this uniform or Labour Camps for those we love. Either . . . or, Madame! No other choice! So for God's sake, give over glaring at us as if we were a couple of cobras, and bring us some coffee.'

"Jan pulled my arm. 'Sit down,' he said. 'You waste your breath.'

"But he was wrong. Oh, the woman went on serving us as if she was praying it would choke us; yet, one day, the sixth of June, I shall always remember it was the sixth of June, she came running out to us, her face white as a sheet.

"'Parlez-vous anglais?' she asked.

"'Mais oui, Madame!' said Jan.

"'Venez! Venez!' she urged.

"Very surprised, we hurried behind her into a room behind the bar. She slammed and bolted the door, and lifted the cover from a sewing-machine. And there was no sewing-machine, but a radio set. And she switched on; and we heard a voice, a calm British voice; and it was saying one sentence, just one beautiful sentence, over and over again:

" 'Under the command of General Eisenhower, Allied Naval Forces, supported by strong Air Forces, began landing Allied Armies this morning on the northern coasts of France.'

" 'Now!' said Jan. 'What's that for a fine idea!' And he sat down, very suddenly.

"And the room was dancing around me too. And I could hear myself saying, 'At last! At last!'

"And the woman was looking at us, and presently she said, in a queer harsh voice, 'So it was true! You were speaking the truth. . . .'

" 'Yes, Madame,' said Jan.

"Then he took out his wallet, and pulled out some money.

" 'Madame, if you could possibly make us up a parcel of food . . . and perhaps a couple of bottles . . .'

" 'Wait here,' said the woman.

"Ten minutes, and she was back with two clumsy parcels.

" 'It's the best I can do,' she said, and abruptly pushed back the money. 'Perhaps, over there in Germany, another woman will do the same for my husband.'

"Then she stood in the doorway, twisting her apron in her rough hands, watching us go. And when we came to the corner, we turned, and saluted her.

"Late that night, Jan and I took the last tram to the outskirts of that little town. And then, on foot, down a quiet road. A long way, a very long way we walked; and at last turned into a forest.

"I walked first, Jan behind. And at every three steps he turned to push back the plants over the little path we were making.

"Then, suddenly, we could go no further. And we sat down under a great bush, and pulled off our boots. My God, were we tired!

"And Jan took out one of the bottles.

" 'Karl!' he said. 'The moment has come! Let us drink to Operation Deserter!'

"Yes, the moment had come, the moment we had prayed for, lived for, planned so minutely, so many, many times!

"We were deserters!

"And we knew that with the Invasion at last on their hands, the Gestapo were not going to have the leisure to go round visiting the families of deserters.

"Besides not all missing soldiers *were* deserters. The Underground Movements were attending to quite a number. And now, of course, they could be safely banked on to improve the shining hour.

"So we had the happiest supper we'd had in years, and then went to sleep under our bush, until the nightingales woke us, shouting to us to be up and on, in the good, safe night.

"Did you ever hear nightingales? The most determined of alarm-clocks! And one cannot switch *them* off.

"Now, if you look at the map, you will think it is very simple to walk from Lorraine straight north into Luxembourg. And so it is, of course—in peace-time. But in war-time, and if one is a deserter, there are complications. Many serious complications.

"However, I knew every kilometre of the way. In my youth I was a vigorous walker. Every holiday I was walking. And best of all, I knew certain farms where I had helped many times with the corn and the hay. Oh yes, I had my list of friends.

"Even so, we had our black days. There was that morning when Jan found he simply could not get his right boot on. His right foot had been giving him trouble for days, and now the whole ball of this foot was no longer a ball, but a balloon, very angry and red. And, of course, Purgatory itself to walk on.

"But I got him to a small farm. The woman there is also from Luxembourg. She was kind enough. She did what she could. But her husband was in hospital with a stomach that led him the life of a dog. Nothing but worry, it seemed.

"And it would hardly have soothed this stomach of his to return and be told there were two German deserters hiding in his loft, being fed by his wife.

"And poor Jan *looks* so Nordic, that square head, the way he talks French. And no use, either, stealing some civilian clothes for him. Nothing would ever fit him. I ask you, more than six foot of him, and size twelve in boots!

"So the moment he could put on his own boot, we went again, with more food, and our bottles filled to the cork.

"But soon, there were nights when we were glad to eat raw potatoes, or push a hen from her nest, and run with the eggs before she got over the shock, and cackled for the dogs.

"And then . . . now, as you see, I can laugh . . . we hid in a train, a Heaven-sent goods-train bound for Luxembourg. We hid among great sacks of corn. And for two days, two nights, that train crawled along, stopping everywhere, simply everywhere!

"The next night, however, there was a sudden commotion. Feet running, voices calling! But nobody came climbing over the sacks; the train began to move off; and we breathed again.

"But the next morning, oh dear Lord in Heaven, the next morning . . . even now I suffocate when I remember it. . . .

"That train, that sacred train had been switched! That was the reason for all the shouting. And now we were going full steam—into Germany! Yes, Germany!

"I tell you, I was demented. Even Jan was white under the dust.

"And all day long, that train did not stop. No, no! Now she was flying, purring like a great cat on her way to Paradise. And all we could do was wait among our sacks, telling each other she would *have* to stop somewhere, sometime.

"She did . . . late that night in a fairly large station.

"Absolute black-out, except for two dim lanterns on the platform.

" 'Listen,' said Jan, and grabbed my arm.

" 'Yes,' I said. 'Yes!'

"At last, at last we could hear them! The great guns of Freedom booming away to the west.

"We waited for a moment; and then crawled out from the sacks, and jumped down to the platform. Nobody saw us. Nobody could see anything a foot away in that blackness. Inch by inch we moved cautiously along. And found ourselves in a queue, a German queue, all soldiers, all ranks, all services, moving slowly forward to the Soldatenheim.

"The Soldatenheim? Oh, it is like your Y.M.C.A.; it provides comfort for the forces.

"And soon, there we were, Jan and I, sitting down in the dark refreshment room, before a bowl of good, hot soup, bread, sausage and thick ersatz coffee.

"Nobody looked at us. All about us were other soldiers, also grey with dust, tired, and unshaven. And the two at our table said that the Americans over there to the west had tanks and guns enough to fit up all Asia and Africa.

"But Jan and I bolted down all that good food. We wanted to hear more, but this was no time for conversation. Any moment, and some officious N.C.O. might come round the tables, demanding to see papers.

"So we went out, as if to the water-closet. But we walked on and on, on the points of our boots, right to the end of the platform. Then over an easy little fence; and there we were, on our way to the Americans!

"And a sudden joy sprang up in me—perhaps it was the good food. And I began to sing the praises of America.

"I said now that was a country, if Jan pleased! All races, all creeds, and dear simplicity itself for the children. They were *all* Americans! Just Americans!

"Oh, the Americans knew better than to condemn a man because his father or his grandfather had been a German!

"The Americans would welcome men like Jan and me! With open arms, they would welcome us!

"But it wasn't precisely simple to find those Americans. Oh, we could hear them all right—the booming, the thunder grew louder and louder. But now, night after night, we had to creep forward like cats. Straying German soldiers were being shot on sight by the S.S. Or hanged. We came across more than one poor devil dangling from a tree; or lying face down in a ditch.

"Then one night we came to a river. And we pushed in the side of a sty—you should have heard the pig! And we took two good planks, and we put all our clothes and our boots on the planks—we had no socks left, of course. And we swam across that river, pushing our planks.

"The next day we were hiding under some bushes high on a hill when, far below us, we saw soldiers.

"But these were not marching as stiff as clockwork,

rechts-links-rechts-links. No, these were moving along with a swing, an easy swing, a swagger, an *American* swagger!

"And we rose to our feet, our throats very dry, and we ran down that hill, shouting, shouting! Shouting!

"To all the stars and stripes of America we shouted in wild and joyous greeting.

"But there was no smile, no welcome on those American faces.

"Silent, very still and alert, they were watching us, guns at the ready.

" 'Kommen Sie mit, Kraut!' called their corporal.

" 'No! No!' I cried. 'This man he is from the Dutch Underground, and I, I am from Luxembourg!'

" 'Oh yeah!' said the American. 'Keep moving! Keep moving!' "

Chapter XVII

A CANADIAN COMES HOME

"No," went on Monsieur Smit, "we were not in the least welcome. No soldier has any use for a deserter. And that is what we were, of course—just two more deserters.

"Neither were the Americans in the mood to listen to the story of our lives—not with all Europe crying aloud, imploring to be liberated.

"But they had to do something about all their German prisoners. So they were sending us all somewhere safe, and setting us to work, until there was time to sort us out.

"And, well, ten days later Jan and I were in Belgium—working down a coal-mine. Yes, yes, a coal-mine.

"I don't like to think of those days, even now. Oh, it wasn't so much the coal-mine; it was that I now knew the terrible taste of despair. Inside my mind, there was nothing but a consuming rage, a great anger against life; and in my bitterness, I would rave that there should be international laws forbidding one nationality to marry into another. Then wars would be such fine simple affairs for the children—no emotional complications, no conflicting loyalties, no being abused, distrusted by both sides! And none of this seeing far too clearly the pity, the terrible pity of it all.

"But Jan was forever arguing back that on the contrary

we mongrels were the hope of the world, the only ones who would ever have the sense to live in peace.

"After a time, however, we no longer argued about anything much. We had not the energy.

"Then something happened that shook me to the soul. The Belgian miners went on strike. But not for themselves. Oh no, in protest against the pitiful rations of food *we prisoners* were receiving!

"I ask you, the Belgians, who have twice in one life-time suffered so much at the hands of the Germans!

"So we were given more food, exactly the same allowance as the Belgians themselves were receiving. But it wasn't only this extra allowance of food that infused me with new courage. No, no, it was the thought that these Belgians had gone on strike . . . for US.

"Then as the days went by, Jan struck up almost a friendship with one of the guards. You know Jan, he would start a conversation with a Sphinx.

"And one day this guard happened to mention that he was a boy of eleven when the 1914 war broke out, and that he was sent to Holland—to Amsterdam.

"'So?' said Jan, very interested, and preparing to have a good talk about the place. 'Now my Dutch grandmother used to live in Amsterdam. She kept a book-shop.'

"'Book-shop?' said the guard. 'What was her name?'

"'Jansen,' said Jan.

"'Where did she live?' asked the guard, suddenly very stiff.

"'In the Vijselstraat,' said Jan.

"'It was a Mevrouw Jansen of the Vijselstraat who took me in,' said the guard, stiffer than ever.

"'Well,' said Jan. 'My grandmother's Christian names were Wilhelmina Adriana.'

" 'Those were her names,' said the guard.

" 'Now!' cried Jan. 'Now! What is this for a fine surprise? Then you must be Pierre . . . Pierre from Brussels!'

" 'Yes,' said the guard, and shot out both hands. And he and Jan shook hands and thumped backs as if they were long-lost brothers."

Monsieur Smit paused, and looked at me.

"You have heard of him, no? This Pierre from Brussels? Yes, yes, that was the boy, the one your Oma looked after, all through the first World War.

"And little did your Oma dream," said Monsieur Smit, very moved indeed, "little did your dear Oma dream that the bread of kindness she cast upon the waters would be found after many years . . . by one Karl Smit of Luxembourg . . . and her own grandson, Jan.

"Yes," went on Monsieur Smit presently, "your Oma's kindness came back to us. For that guard, Pierre of Brussels, immediately set to work to help us. He wrote letters. He cycled kilometres to see important people. He sat down on their doorsteps until they listened to him. He found a way of getting a message through to the Dutch Underground Movement, and the Resistance of Luxembourg. And they, of course, sent back the strongest messages on our behalf.

"And when Christmas came, we kissed Pierre from Brussels on both cheeks, and went home—home to Luxembourg and my family! We were free! Free!

"I cannot tell you what this means. All I can say is that it is a feeling like no other; perhaps one then catches a glimpse of what the good God has in mind for us all . . . if only we have the sense to recognise it.

"But poor Jan was still far from happy. He still had no

news of his family in Holland. The Allies had stormed through the north of France, through Belgium, and one Sunday, the third of September . . . I have a good memory for dates . . . they reached the Dutch frontier!

"And outside every Dutch town, the people waited with flowers, ready to welcome their Liberators. But only the darkness came; and they had to return to their houses, their cellars, their sheds. But, 'To-morrow, they'll come!' they said. 'To-morrow they will be here!'

"But to-morrow came and went; and Holland still waited . . .

"Then came the tragedy of Arnhem. And summer crawled into autumn, damp and wretched, and still the whole west of Holland was under the Nazis. And they knew they were cornered, and that made them all the more vicious. And that year, if you remember, it rained and rained. All the crops in Holland were drowned; and the floods, the prices, the misery, rose higher and higher.

"We tried to cheer Jan up.

"'Och,' we said. 'It can't be long now! It simply cannot be long!'

"Then the winter came, and soon the papers were reporting such hunger in Occupied Holland that the breweries were no longer brewing beer, but soup made of turnip-peelings and tulip-bulbs.

"And when spring came, there was no electricity there, no gas, no food, no medicine, no coffins. But still the starving Dutch said, 'They'll come!'

"And at last, of course, they came!

"Yes, on Monday, the seventh of May, at ten minutes past five, a beautiful sight went rumbling down the main avenue of Rotterdam. It was a tank, a Canadian tank! And there were children riding all over it, and dancing and running by its sides. And the people, the sober Dutch people, wept and sang to see it, as if it were a chariot from Heaven itself . . . as indeed it was.

"And well," said Monsieur Smit, blowing his nose, "three days later your Cousin Jan was knocking at his mother's door, just in time for her birthday!"

"Yes, I know," I said, and laughed aloud as I wiped my eyes.

"Ah! so you have heard of what we arranged, eh?" chuckled Monsieur Smit. "Jolly fine show, no?"

"Yes," I choked. "Oh, yes!"

It was indeed a fine show, and Heaven alone knows how they arranged it; that is Heaven, Monsieur Smit, Jan and three sympathetic Canadian soldiers alone know how they arranged it. But my cousin Jan, who had gone marching out of Holland, a German conscript, his heart in his heavy German army-boots, came riding back to Rotterdam on a Canadian lorry, dressed from head to foot as a Canadian! Yes, as a Canadian soldier, his heart as light as a feather under his maple-leaf—and almost note-perfect in "Oh, Canada" on a Canadian mouth-organ kindly lent to him by the driver of the lorry.

Now maybe you've already gathered that come rain, come shine, the Dutch obstinately insist on celebrating a birthday. And that year, Mynheer Vos was most anxious to make the tenth of May a truly happy occasion.

To begin with, Tanta Joh would be seventy. And outside, after fifty desolate months, the red, white and blue flags of the Netherlands danced and fluttered once more from every window.

But in Tanta Joh's eyes there was still a great sorrow. She had lost two of her beloved step-sons; and now she was convinced she would never see Jan again.

But she was not the one to spoil another's pleasure. So she brought down extra chairs from the bedrooms, and set them round the table in her sitting-room; and she got out all that was left of her best china; put on her best frock, and all day long she cheerfully welcomed the friends and neighbours who called in to wish her a happy birthday.

About seven o'clock that evening, their sitting-room was crowded. There were Tanta Joh's two step-sons and their wives; there were our three Dutch cousins and their husbands, there were . . . well, it will be far quicker to say there was hardly room for another. And Mynheer Vos, very proud and happy, was about to pull the cork of a very special bottle, when there was a thunderous banging on the street-door.

My cousin, Mina, put her head out of the window.

"Tanta!" she cried. "There's a Canadian soldier out there on the step!"

"A Canadian!" said Mynheer Vos, and looked out too.

And yes, there stood a tall Canadian, carrying a great bouquet of red roses.

"Yes, sir?" asked Mynheer Vos in his careful English. "Can we perhaps help you?"

"Ja!" roared the Canadian. "Ja, Vader! You can come and open this door! I want to kiss my mother!"

And he threw back his head and yelled: "Mutti! Hello there, Mutti!"

Mutti! Tanta Joh's hands flew to her throat. Only Jan . . . only Jan . . . called her Mutti.

And pushing them all aside, she ran to the door and threw it open.

"Now may God be praised!" she wept. "My son! My own dear son!"

Now Tanta Joh lives in a very quiet suburb, almost a village, and the news of Jan's arrival spread like wild-fire. One neighbour ran to tell another, and they sent the children galloping round to tell the others. And they knocked up Mynheer Bolmers who keeps the flower-shop there, and he hastily re-opened his shop and began to do a roaring trade. You see, the Dutch *know* they are not very good at saying what they feel, and at moments like this they bring along flowers to express what lies deep in their hearts. And Tanta Joh's neighbours knew everything; they knew why Jan had gone into Hitler's army, they knew about the doctor who had broken his arm and leg to defer his bitter call-up. And so they wanted flowers to offer him as they shook by him the hand, and joked, "Broken any good bones lately?" The rest, of course, they left unsaid.

But soon, Tanta Joh's sitting-room was full of flowers— bowls, baskets, bunches of flowers.

And in came Mynheer Snel, the photographer, and they all squeezed out of the way whilst he took a photograph. Tanta Joh sent us all copies. I have mine on my desk as I write. There stands Jan, in his fine Canadian uniform, one arm about Tanta Joh, the other about his step-father.

And to either side, and banked high behind them, are the flowers, the lovely, welcoming, Dutch flowers!

Very, very late that night when all the neighbours had gone home, Tanta Joh went upstairs to put the best sheets on Jan's bed. Suddenly she gave a little cry, and ran to the chest of drawers, and took out a letter.

"Jan! Jan!" she called. "All this has driven it out of my head! But here's a letter for you. It came through the Red Cross three months ago. It's from France!"

"From France!" said Jan; and opened it very slowly, as if half afraid of what might be inside.

Then Tanta Joh, anxiously watching his face, saw it light up again in a wide, affectionate smile.

"Well, for crying out loud!" said my Canadian cousin. "If it isn't from my old friend, Monsieur Pacoret! Yes, the French ironmonger who lives at the Ironmongery of the Rue Saint Louis half way down the Rue de la République!"

And Jan sat down on his bed and translated:

Dear Monsieur and Friend,

You once gave me the address of your family in Holland. You said one never knew, even I might find myself travelling there one day.

But I must confess that when I entered this address in my book, it was from pure force of habit. I little dreamed that I should one day send a letter there, and pray that you would be spared to read it.

Yet this is precisely what I am now doing. I am devoutly praying that you will one day hold this letter in your hands, and read it.

First I must tell you that both my dear sisters are dead, within three months of each other, and both very peacefully, thank God. And it is now my duty to inform you that they have remembered you in their joint will. So when this terrible war is over, will you please communicate with me, giving me your permanent address.

My wife and I often speak of you and wonder how you are. We, ourselves, are safe and well.

Believe me, we shall be most happy to have news of you. With a thousand friendly greetings, and a vigorous handshake.

Your old friend and client,

GASTON PACORET.

"Well!" said Tanta Joh, very interested indeed. "Now I wonder what they have left you?"

"Ornaments!" said Jan promptly. "Ornaments from Indo-China. They had a whole mantelpiece full of them in the sitting-room. They inherited them from an uncle. And I used to stand in front of them and say they positively fascinated me. And Mademoiselle Victorine, very pleased, used to say they would leave me a pair in their will. And which two would I prefer? And I used to say it was impossible to decide, they all fascinated me . . . but not in the way they supposed, I'm afraid."

"Ah well," sympathised Mynheer Vos, "you can always persuade some hard-up museum to accept them."

"He'll doing nothing of the sort," cried my Tanta Joh, absolutely scandalised. "He must keep them, of course. The very idea!"

Mynheer Vos looked at her indignant face, and laughed aloud.

"Jan," he said, "I warn you! She is thinking that one has to begin somewhere. For those ornaments you will need a mantelpiece, in a room, in a house; and then, of course, a wife to dust the lot!"

"And about time, too!" said my Tanta Joh.

And once again she threw her arms about her son, and hugged him close.

Chapter XVIII

HÔTEL-RESTAURANT DE LA VICTOIRE

The next day Jan sat down to write a letter to our Cousin Philippe in Marseilles.

This in itself was unusual, for Jan never wrote a letter if a card would do. Moreover it seems he tore up half a dozen before he was satisfied.

Dear Philippe,

This comes to say I am back in Holland with the family. They are all safe. At the moment they all look thin, but every day there is a little more food, so soon, please God, they will all be fine again.

Now, how are you and your children? And how is poor Paul's wife? Write soon and give us plenty of news. And photographs too, if possible. That would please us all, especially of course my mother. You know how she loves photographs.

Philippe, I cannot blow a whistle to reach your ears. So this letter must do for a whistle for help. Yes, I need your help in something important to me.

Can you now give me the name and address of the French woman, the one I once pushed into the gateway of a gas-works.

You will ask why. Let us say I wish to apologise for pushing a lady.

Heartiest greetings from us all to you all.

Your affectionate cousin,

JAN.

Jan then braced himself with a cup of good Canadian coffee, and wrote yet another letter. This one was to his old friend Monsieur Pacoret.

And in it he wrote that he had now safely received Monsieur Pacoret's letter, and that he was truly happy to learn that both he and Madame, his wife, were safe and well.

He was, however, very grieved to learn of the deaths of his two old friends, Mademoiselle Victorine and Mademoiselle Herminie.

Monsieur Pacoret must nevertheless be deeply grateful now to reflect on their quiet happy years of retirement at "Mon Repos".

Here Jan paused and thought hard about the ornaments from Indo-China. Then he held out his cup for more coffee, filled his pen to gain still more time; and then wrote that he was indeed touched, truly touched, to learn that Mademoiselle Victorine and Mademoiselle Herminie had remembered him in their will. Not that he needed any souvenir to remind him of all the pleasant talks he had enjoyed so many times in the dear old ironmongery of the Rue Saint Louis, of which, by the way, he still had that fine photograph taken on Monsieur Pacoret's wedding-day.

But to come back to the souvenir so kindly left him, he knew he could ask Monsieur Pacoret to keep it for the time being. His plans were a little vague and uncertain at the moment, but he was hoping to be back in France soon. Then maybe Monsieur Pacoret would pack it up and send it on to him there.

In conclusion, he was very much hoping that one day he would again have the very real pleasure of calling on Monsieur Pacoret and Madame, his wife—not as a commercial traveller, however, but as their old and, believe him, very affectionate friend, Jan Bauer.

Our Cousin Philippe wrote back by return of post.

Dear old Jan,

Enchanted to hear the so-good news! But of all this, and also all our news, I will write on Sunday. Tell Tanta Joh I will also send photographs.

To-day, I hurry to inform you that I never knew the real name of the woman you saved with your push. We all went by assumed names. All I know is that the others always referred to her as "Sparrow".

I will write immediately to these others—those who are left, not many, alas!

I assure you, Jan, I will do all my possible, but it may take a little time.

Colette joins me in a big kiss for Tanta Joh, and friendliest greetings to you all.

Till Sunday, then!
PHILIPPE.

Jan, however, was not prepared to wait patiently in Holland whilst Philippe did "all his possible" to trace Sparrow in France.

About a month later, this curious advertisement began to appear every day in a certain French provincial newspaper:

To SPARROW. Ouwe Klare, not Tip van Bootz, waiting every evening same place. Earnestly desires continue conversation.

And our Cousin Jan had kissed his mother, shaken hands warmly with the rest of our family in Holland, and concluded certain financial arrangements with our Cousin Philippe—in those days no one was allowed to take more than five pounds out of Holland. In short, he had suffered no grass whatever to grow under his impatient feet, and calling, "Till next year!" he had set out once more . . . to that little French town set among vineyards with the high range of hills to the south, thick with forests and honeycombed with caves. And now very quiet and tranquil beneath the blue sky.

He took a room in Hôtel-Restaurant de la Victoire, a modest establishment right opposite the park—proprietor, Monsieur August Portier.

And Monsieur Auguste Portier and Madame, his wife, were soon deeply intrigued to observe that this tall, middle-aged visitor from Holland always tore through his excellent dinner at a speed that must have played the very devil with his digestion. Indeed, as Madame said, one would imagine he was an American seeing France in three days. And then, if one pleased, he would get up, and walk across the road into the park. And come walking back just after the clock of the Town Hall struck midnight, alone! Always alone.

"Now what, in the name of thunder, can he find to do all those hours in the park?" mused Monsieur Portier. "Unless he's a botanist or something else bizarre. I once heard of a man who did nothing but gape at moths. Yes, maybe it's moths!"

"Nonsense! He is not the type!" decided Madame. "One

doesn't put on one's best suit, brush one's hair, shine up one's shoes, bolt one's good dinner, to study moths. And that *is* his best suit. It hangs behind his door all day. Very good-quality cloth, pre-war, of course. And there's a Dutch tailor's label inside the jacket.

"No, no, I tell you he is a mystery, that one, and no mistake."

Meanwhile the mystery was walking along the path by the side of the little stream that flows through the lovely park. Presently, he came to the place where it tumbles in a waterfall over the mossy rocks. He climbed down the flight of stone steps, and walked to the long bench under the trees, facing the waterfall. And sat down to wait, his head in a newspaper.

And all about him, the children played and chattered, till presently their mothers began to call, "Ah non! Veux-tu te dépêcher enfin?"

And one by one, they straggled off home, still chattering like sparrows.

Then it was dusk. And the lovers came strolling under the trees, arms about each other. And looked at that man occupying that delectable bench. As if there weren't other benches all over the park suitable for the middle-aged to sit and read newspapers. Ah non, alors!

But Jan sat on.

And presently it was night. And over there in the darkness, the waterfall sang and splashed. "I love this place," it sang. "I love this place. . . ."

And Jan waited there, listening . . . listening . . .

Suddenly the great clock of the Town Hall began to strike twelve. And Jan got up, cold and stiff, and walked slowly back to the Hôtel-Restaurant de la Victoire.

And as he went up the stairs, Monsieur Portier called, "Bonne nuit, Monsieur!"; and he would think, "Well, if it isn't moths, what the devil is it? A sensible type like that doesn't *walk* all night in a park!"

On the seventh night as Jan sat there on that bench, for no reason at all, he suddenly felt infinitely tired.

And it seemed to him that all the grey fears and doubts he had thrust so resolutely from him for so many weary months came crowding about him, crying aloud that he was wasting his time, that he could not hope to see her again.

Why not face facts?

Maybe he had always been wrong. Maybe he had always wasted his time; junketing round, seeking to lay hands on some elusive happiness, just beyond his reach.

Maybe one always paid in the end for this refusal to make do, to accept the next-best.

And he tried to think clearly about all this, to probe his restless mind; but the hunger in his heart would have none of this sterile analysis.

He only knew that he was waiting there, longing most desperately to hear the voice of a woman of whom he knew next to nothing—save that he loved her.

And she might well be married by now, or . . .

But no, she was not dead. He didn't know how, or why he knew it, but he *knew* she was not dead.

It was then that he heard it—a faint rustle. He turned; and there, at the end of the bench, sat a woman, her head in a newspaper.

"Well, Monsieur," said a quiet voice. "Shall we continue the conversation?"

And oh, to Jan it was as if every nightingale in France had burst into song.

But, "Now! Now!" stammered that cousin of mine. "What is this for a fine surprise!"

And this, I am afraid, is all I am able to report of that conversation, so long delayed, except that it was all of midnight before it was over, and my Cousin Jan and "Sparrow" came walking together out of the park—and just in the nick of time, too; the keeper had already locked up the two side gates.

It also seems that across the road, outside the Hôtel-Restaurant de la Victoire, Monsieur and Madame Portier were enjoying the cool air and a heated game of cards with their two friends Monsieur Bertier, the chemist, and Monsieur Brunet who struggles daily with English Literature in the Lycée for Boys.

Suddenly, Madame Portier gave a little shriek and sat bolt upright in her chair.

"Don't all turn round at once," she implored, "but take a little look at that tall type now coming out of the park. Yes, yes, the one smiling with all his teeth, and with his arm about a little woman. And this will make you twist on your chairs, my poor Auguste here would have it he goes to the park every night to study moths!

"Mon Dieu! He is bringing her over here to us!"

And yes, Jan was bringing "Sparrow" over to them.

"Madame, Messieurs," he was saying, "permit me to introduce the woman I love and whom I was beginning to fear I should never see again. So I know I may invite you all to drink our health in a glass of champagne. A bottle of the very best you have, if you please, Madame."

Well, as Monsieur Brunet was to express it later on, the French may have their little faults, who hasn't? but they are at least a sympathetic race, as swift to hold out both hands to a dramatic situation as to a dramatic bottle.

And here were two people, no longer young, but positively shining with a most moving new happiness, not to mention the generous desire to share a bottle of good champagne. Two bottles, to be exact.

Small wonder then that Monsieur Brunet considers he made the speech of his life on that memorable night. It is, of course, a thousand pities that nobody, not even Monsieur Brunet himself, can recall all he said. But his peroration will live for ever in all their memories.

"Over there in Britain," said Monsieur Brunet, accepting another glass of champagne, "they have a writer who swears happy people are not interesting. Now I know you will all agree that Monsieur here, and Mademoiselle, his charming companion, absolutely refute this lugubrious statement. Let us confess we find them deeply interesting. It is not every night that such happiness comes walking across the road to us—a bottle of champagne under each arm.

No, no, I myself prefer a much older adage:

> *In water, one sees but one's own face,*
> *In wine, one beholds the heart of another.*"

And Monsieur Brunet peered into his glass, and then raised it high, and cried, "Long live happiness! May we never be too old to recognise it!"

Chapter XIX

THE HAPPY SPARROW

Two months later we all received a formal printed card from France which announced the marriage "dans la plus stricte intimité" of Mademoiselle Marie Thérèse Martin and Monsieur Jan Bauer.

My husband, studying this, said the French certainly had the oddest way of saying that the wedding had been nice and quiet.

On the back of the card, however, was another of Jan's compact messages:

Very happy. Now looking for place to live. Hope to see you all there one day. Much affection.

MARIE-THÉRÈSE AND JAN.

Our next news came from Tanta Joh. She wrote that they had not been able to travel to France to see Jan married at last, not so much because of these wretched currency restrictions, but because Mynheer Vos was only now getting over a very nasty attack of bronchitis.

However, thank the dear Lord, Jan's wife sounded a truly warm-hearted, sensible woman. She had sent them a really beautiful letter; and Jan himself had staggered and delighted them with the very longest letter of his life. And the most surprising!

Among the wedding presents, wrote Jan, there had been a large wooden box from Monsieur Pacoret. And there inside, as Jan feared, were two of the largest and most hideous ornaments from the mantelpiece of the sitting-room of the Ironmongery of the Rue Saint Louis—once the pride and joy of Mademoiselles Herminie and Victorine.

But that was not all. There was also a long registered letter from Monsieur Pacoret himself.

He said Madame Pacoret joined wholeheartedly with him in wishing Jan and his wife every possible happiness. They had been delighted to receive the photograph of Marie-Thérèse which Jan had sent them. And all Monsieur Pacoret would say was that Jan had again showed that felicitous "flair" for which they, too, would be eternally grateful.

But now, Monsieur Pacoret had a surprise for Jan, a financial surprise, which would shortly be confirmed by Monsieur Pacoret's lawyer.

Mademoiselle Herminie and Mademoiselle Victorine had also left Jan a comfortable sum of money!

"I will be frank," wrote honest Monsieur Pacoret. "At first I was staggered, and even a little vexed. Never before have we Pacorets left one sou of our money outside the family. But this war has taught us all many lessons. However, I will not moralize. I will only say that both my wife and I have now come to the conclusion that my dear sisters had every right to leave some of their own money to whom they pleased, to choose their own way of expressing their appreciation of your friendly advice and help on more than one occasion.

"We, of course, were their only relatives; and to us they have left all their Government Bonds and their shares in the business. I am telling you this so that the position may be clear to you, and you may freely accept this gift which is yours, both legally and morally. With it, I assure you, come all our good wishes.

"I must, however, point out that I agree absolutely with the one condition in my dear sisters' will. This money was earned in France. It must now be invested, or spent, in our country. We, ourselves, think it may be enough to purchase a small house, or a business, not at iniquitous Paris prices, of course, but somewhere in the provinces.

"But whatever you decide, may it bring you both much true joy and happiness. This, my dear friend, is the sincere wish of both

PAULETTE AND GASTON PACORET."

Jan sent this letter to Tanta Joh and she sent it all round the family. So, a month or so later, we were not in the least surprised to receive one of Jan's picture postcards, announcing that he and Marie-Thérèse were going to make their home in France.

But we *were* surprised to receive another postcard later on that announced they had decided to settle down in a village in the south of France in a district known as Le Gard.

By and by, we all began to receive picture postcards of this village—the church, the post office, the War Memorial, the bandstand on the market-square. And it certainly looked the quietest place.

Moreover, on the backs of these postcards, Jan began to write the oddest scraps of news:

Just bought two goats.

Or: Forgive silence. Very busy with apricots at the moment.

Or: Vines doing well this year.

On every single postcard, however, he always wrote: Fine place for holiday, this! Delighted to see any of you at any time.

Nobody in the family took these invitations seriously, of course. We simply could not see Jan settling down in any village for long, especially as his postcards left us in the dark about what he found to *do* there—apart from the goats, the apricots, and the vines.

No, we all had the feeling that Jan's next postcard might well run: Money run out. Off to Algeria . . . or Rhodesia. Excellent job. Fine prospects.

But we were wrong.

The picture postcards still arrived, still the same village. And now Jan began to add quite poetical inducements to his "Fine place for holiday, this!"

He would write: Excellent fishing, here!

Or: Mountain air. Vast horizons.

And once he even wrote: Complete repose.

That shook the family, I can tell you. Complete repose! Our Cousin Jan!

My husband, I was quick to notice, seemed more than interested in the "Excellent fishing here!" So one day last May, I was able to send a triumphant picture postcard— Piccadilly Circus—to Jan and Marie-Thérèse. And on the back I wrote:

"Persuaded my husband to take holiday in South of France this year. Hope to call in and see you both, and the vast horizons, some time early in June."

And one lovely evening, there we stood, my husband and I, on the deserted market square of that quiet French village, and looked about us.

There was the little bandstand, the church, the post office, the War Memorial . . . just as on Jan's postcards.

"Must be over there," I decided. "He once said, 'Conveniently next door to Bureau of Tobacco'."

"But that's a café!" objected my husband.

"Look at its name!" I said.

There, over the door of that café, in bold black capitals, it said:

Café du Moineau Heureux.

Café of the Happy Sparrow.

So we crossed over, pushed aside the long bead curtain in the doorway, and walked inside.

Behind a high wooden counter stood a plump, pleasant-looking woman, busily polishing glasses.

"Is it . . . Marie-Thérèse?" I asked.

She threw down her cloth and flung out both hands.

"So you've come at last! Ah, Jean will be so happy! Your room is ready since May! Jean! Jean! Come quickly, my Jeannot! They are here!"

Out from a door to one side of the counter shot a tall, burly man, his brown face one vast welcoming smile.

"Now!" said my Cousin Jan. "Now! What is this for a good surprise! What a fine surprise!"

"But sit down, sit down," sang Marie-Thérèse. "Get glasses, my Jeannot! And we will eat supper and talk!"

And talk we did, all that evening and far into the night.

We spent the whole of that holiday with Jan and Marie-Thérèse. They simply would not hear of our travelling on. So we missed every one of the sights a conscientious tourist ought to see for his money. But never, never have we had so happy a holiday.

There was something so pleasant about the Café du Moineau Heureux, something kind and homely, that went straight to our hearts. Maybe it was Marie-Thérèse's warm eagerness to make us feel at home, the swift gay way of her as she joked and laughed and sang, the rare gift she had for drawing the warmth out of others. Faces lit up when Marie-Thérèse came into a room; there was simply no feeling dull or uninteresting when she was about.

As for Jan, he was never the one to parade his affections, but I noticed how he would call to his wife every time he came in.

"Marie-Thérèse!" he would shout. "Where the devil *is* the woman?"

And Marie-Thérèse would come bustling in, as delighted as if he were shouting his love aloud to the sound of trumpets. As indeed he was, he unmistakably was.

Then the village was far bigger and far, far lovelier than we had imagined from the postcards. It straggled all round the market-square, and then on and up to the mountain slopes beyond, where fig-trees grew as wild as you please between great carpets of wild lavender and thyme.

And there were vineyards everywhere—every family seemed to own at least one, as well as an orchard of peach and apricot trees.

And we had all our meals on one of the tables set on the pavement outside the café. Nobody seems to waste fresh air and sunshine in that part of France. And everybody passing by would call, "Bon appétit!" and we'd call back "Merci!" And one word simply didn't lead to another in that village, it led to long, leisurely conversations. And the sun shone warmer and warmer in the cloudless sky, and presently we would push our table over into the shade of a great lime tree in full flower; and a little wind would come dancing down from the mountains, filling all the air with the perfume of thyme and lavender and the warm tang of the lime.

And Marie-Thérèse, very flushed and proud, would come bustling out, crying, "Now, taste me this", and set yet another delicious masterpiece before us.

As for what Jan found to do there . . .!

Well, there was a very large room behind the café itself, where every evening of the week something or another seemed to be going full swing.

On Mondays, for instance, it was reserved for the Loyal Republicans of France. And all seventeen of them carefully explained that we simply must not be misled by the name. They were, at heart, staunch right-wing Conservatives, absolutely brothers-in-politics to Weenston Churcheel himself.

On Fridays, the opposition met there—the United Socialist Front. It seemed that they really met in a rival café just across the square, but Madame its proprietor had been obliged to go to Nîmes to nurse an aged aunt—and certain legitimate expectations. So Jan had a gentleman's agreement with her till such time as she returned, with, one trusted, all expectations satisfactorily concluded. Meanwhile the United Socialists were meeting at "The Happy Sparrow". And Monsieur Tavat, their president, took us on one side and conscientiously explained that we were not to be taken in by titles—they were the only true republicans, *liberal* republicans of the old school of thought, brothers-in-spirit to George Washington himself.

And my husband's face was a study when Marie-Thérèse told us that Jan had made quite a name for himself at the last election. He had obligingly written all the proclamations and election-addresses for both parties.

"Both?" queried my husband, unable to believe his ears.

Marie-Thérèse proudly said yes, indeed. All these politicians had to do was sketch in the bold outlines of what they wanted to publish to the world. Jan was the artist they engaged, as it were, to fill in the canvas with glowing words and grandiose phrases.

Everybody in those parts, it seemed, adored a fine resounding speech. And when elections were in the air, then vaï! they really let rip! No pale, oblique innuendoes for them. They liked their speeches spicy and slanderous with plenty of offence meant, and plenty taken. And the most pungent of insults flying like shuttlecocks from one platform to the other.

And there, right on the spot now, was my Cousin Jan, free as air, a born speech-writer, not giving a damn for any party, and therefore to be relied on to give both sides equal measure of the strong stuff such as "Judas kiss, moral turpitude, despicable nepotism", nicely balanced with a rousing fifty per cent each of the time-honoured appeals to "Oh, Democracy, thou shrine of man's bright hopes!" and "Oh, France, take up thy sword! Defend thy peaceful policies!"

Oh yes, already a most valuable man politically in that village, my cousin Jan.

But to come back to that large room behind the café. On Tuesday evenings, "La Sainte Cécile" gathered there. "La Sainte Cécile" was the village brass-band as well as the fire-brigade. And Jan, if you please, had a finger in both pies. He had charge of the drum; and the fire-engine, a hand one, circa 1910, was kept in the shed where he stored his logs for the winter.

We, fortunately, did not see a fire; but every Tuesday evening we would sit outside "The Happy Sparrow" enjoying the air whilst "La Sainte Cécile" treated us to "Sambre et Meuse" and "The Daughter of the Regiment" and other stirring melodies—with suitable intervals for refreshment, of course.

Then there was the Bowling Club. Now they seemed to meet every night of the week. They played on a stretch of ground at the back of the café between Jan's vegetable garden and his apricot orchard. And again I'll never forget my husband's face as he inspected it. It was none of your English green lawns as smooth as velvet, but a long patch of hard, well-trodden earth down which they rolled their battered wooden bowls—and even they were plainly not as round as they used to be.

Then there was the village priest, Monsieur le Curé, a round exuberant gentleman with a lively sense of humour. He was on excellent terms with Jan, and they both said we simply must step in one day and inspect the church.

"It's not ancient," apologised Monsieur le Curé. "Barely two hundred years old. But we have something altogether singular in mural paintings—a 'Last Judgment' that is really remarkable."

It was indeed! It was a brightly coloured painting that ran right along one wall—all the smug and smiling Saved in pink and blue robes to the right of the Throne, all the truly villainous Lost howling and grovelling in grey sackcloth and ashes to the left.

"Painted about eighty years ago," said Monsieur le Curé, "by an artistic retired Deputy who was also a brisk quarreller. So all the faces to the right are those of his best friends, and all the Lost to the left are unmistakably those of his colleagues who refused to agree with him.

"At the time it made an uproarious scandal, I can tell you. Deputies up there in Paris came to blows about it. There was even some talk of a duel to the death; but then the Prussians started their war, and there were other matters to quarrel about."

At this moment, the children of the Catechism Class came clattering in, so we thanked Monsieur le Curé, and turned to go.

"We will meet again to-night, of course!" cried Monsieur le Curé. "I warn you, the Patronage are determined to show you we can do these things almost as well as in your West End!"

Now the Patronage was the Boys' Club, run by Monsieur le Curé. And on that evening they were to give a Repeat Gala Performance, in our honour, of one of their recent successes: Sherlock Holmes and the Rajah's Rubies.

So there we sat that evening—with all the Patronage's friends and relations, packed tightly together on long wooden benches in Jan's large room, applauding the lynx-eyed Shair-lock Olm-ez who every now and then grinned at my husband and me, and burst into snatches of English. At least I was just going to ask Marie-Thérèse if it was English, when she gave me a nudge.

"Jan taught him his English," she whispered, eyes shining with pride.

My husband muttered that this explained about every-thing; and that he'd never heard a music-hall turn yet to beat that French lad speaking English with a heavy Dutch-German accent, especially his:

Vai-taire! Breng ros-bif mit pouding en von pot off tea en Bismarck about eet! Dok-teur Vatsohn en I aire dam on-gree.

But the Rajah's Rubies were not the only sparkling jewels of that memorable evening. When all the benches had been stacked away in their shed again, the Patronage and the audience went merrily off home, but Monsieur le Curé lingered behind, chatting of this and that, and not in the least inclined, it seemed to me, to hurry back to his bleak little presbytery.

Presently from the kitchen came the clatter of plates, the good smell of soup, and the voice of Marie-Thérèse:

"Monsieur le Curé, why not stay and have a bite of supper with us? In the kitchen, and no ceremony whatever! And only an omelette, but I can promise you the soup will be good—it's one of my specials!"

"Yes, do stay," urged Jan. "It's not every night we have visitors from England."

"No, indeed," said Monsieur le Curé; and face beaming with pleasure he promptly walked into the kitchen and pulled up a chair to the table.

Two hours later we had enthusiastically polished off the special soup, a dream of an omelette, a beautiful cheese made of goat's milk, and a great bowl of ripe cherries. Not to mention three bottles of wine, the Entente Cordiale, Marshall Aid, Atlantic Defence, the French Fiscal System, Uno, Unesco, and the latest in governments.

And now Marie-Thérèse was busy at her stove making the coffee; and Jan, watching her, said this was the solemn hour of the day when she always reminded him of Madame Curie intent on her retorts and test-tubes.

Marie-Thérèse, pouring out the coffee, said of all the

rubbish, especially coming from a man who had never had the honour of setting eyes on Madame Curie.

And Jan said maybe not, but he'd take his dying oath the expression was precisely the same—all rapt exaltation, if we knew what he meant.

Monsieur le Curé, giving a first reverent sip, sighed yes, but surely one needed vision to turn out anything superlative.

And Marie-Thérèse, very gratified, was turning to put the coffee-back on the stove, when she whirled round again and cried, "Té! I suppose you have heard, Monsieur le Curé, that Madame Didier's stove has arrived!"

"Of course!" said Monsieur le Curé, and he and Jan gave a great guffaw.

So I asked what was so amusing about Madame Didier's stove. And Monsieur le Curé said it wasn't precisely the stove itself—Madame Didier having had the good sense to consult Jan about that before she ordered it from a reliable firm up there in Saint Etienne. No, no, it was the manner of its arrival that was now causing the whole village to twist so with laughter.

"You may have noticed," went on Monsieur le Curé, wiping his eyes, "that we are fortunate enough to have a local railway line here, not exactly important, I admit, but extremely handy."

We said yes, come to think of it, we had noticed a grass-grown railway track and a level-crossing on a lonely road some way outside the village. But though we had some-times caught a distant chuffing as we strolled home to supper of an evening, we had not, as yet, set eyes on a train.

"But I assure you we have one!" cried Monsieur le Curé. "It arrives every evening about a quarter past seven, or near enough. And it always stops for a moment at that little house there, and the driver descends to take a little glass of 'pastis' with old Marius—he's in charge of the crossing, of course."

"Good lord!" breathed my husband.

"And why not?" demanded Marie-Thérèse. "Nobody in our train is ever in much of a hurry."

"Heavens, no!" agreed Monsieur le Curé. "They've more sense than that, I hope!

"But to come back to our little comedy. The days went by, and still Madame Didier had no news of her stove. So she wrote a very indignant letter to the firm in Saint Etienne. And they wrote back, by return of post, saying they had definitely dispatched Madame's esteemed order; and they enclosed the railway-chit to prove it.

"So Madame Didier sat down again and wrote a fiery letter to the Railways of France. And they replied that the stove had most certainly been sent off, and was therefore indubitably en route. But they would forthwith begin a little inquiry into this singular delay.

"So Madame Didier waited. And waited. And when she could endure it no longer, she would sit down and write yet another fiery letter to the Railways of France, who would then politely send her yet another carbon copy of their first letter.

"But the day came when Madame Didier could wait no longer. She simply had to go to Marseilles where her married daughter was daily expecting her fourth.

"But before she went she called on her neighbour, Félix Corsin—he's something of a plumber as well as a barber. And Félix agreed to take charge of her front door key, to take delivery of the stove when it turned up, and to fix it up in her kitchen when he had a moment to spare.

"Now yesterday was the day of the month when Félix cuts hair and does odd jobs of plumbing up there in Saint Gilles of the Mountain. And he was cycling back home along that road to our level crossing when he saw our train standing there. And there was the driver just disappearing into the little house to have his quiet glass with old Marius. Nothing astonishing about all this, of course. But as luck would have it, there, drawn up right in front of Félix, was the luggage van, its guardian sitting on the steps, tranquilly rolling a cigarette.

"When they'd passed the time of the day, something prompted Félix to ask if the guard had heard anything of a kitchen-stove lately.

" 'Stove?' said the guard. 'Té! Is it yours then, that stove?'

" 'Which stove?' asked Félix. He's a cautious type; comes from somewhere up there in the North.

" 'The one we've got on board, of course!' said the guard, waving a careless hand towards the dark interior of his van.

" 'Addressed here to Madame Widow Didier?' asked Félix.

" 'Now you mention it,' said the guard, 'I believe it is.'

" 'Good!' said Félix. 'I've promised to take delivery.'

"And he crossed over, and between them, they got out the stove and set it down on the side of the track.

" 'Name of a pipe, but she's dusty!' panted Félix.

" 'Naturally!' grunted the guard. 'So would you be after weeks on end playing the shuttlecock up and down this damn line.'

" 'Listen,' said Félix, refusing to believe his Northern ears. 'You're not telling me this stove's been jaunting to and fro all this time in that van of yours?'

" 'Monsieur!' said the guard with infinite dignity, 'pray correct me if I am wrong, but did it, or did it not take two of us to get her down just now?

" 'And I happen to have but one pair of arms, Monsieur, only one pair, no more!

" 'I was naturally waiting till someone turned up some time to lend me a hand.' "

When the laughter had died down a little, my husband began to say he would always be grateful he had heard this story on the spot as it were.

And when pressed to explain, he said that over there in England he had considerable difficulty in swallowing anything unusual. But here, maybe it was the sun or their excellent little wine, but whatever it was, even the truth, so help him, seemed brighter and better than fiction. And far more digestible.

Now through the open window I could see the plane trees on the silent market-square, burnished now, and so silver and serene in the moonlight that I sighed oh yes, indeed, and that I myself felt it must be Heaven itself to live in their tranquil, lovely village.

Monsieur le Curé, very alarmed, put down his cup.

"My poor Madame!" he cried. "You positively frighten me! You make it sound as if you were convinced our desirable village had transformed us, en masse, into celestial characters.

"Alas, Madame, it is my painful duty to inform you that we are deplorably like other people, no better, no worse, and with perhaps even more of a relish for shouting for reforms . . . in others, of course.

"Indeed," went on Monsieur le Curé, sadly accepting

a small glass of brandy, "though I would not risk confiding this to everyone, I myself have a certain reluctant respect for Satan. I am in a position to know, and I assure you he never hangs round anywhere just kicking his hoofs."

My husband said that seemed fair enough to him, and that he supposed it made Life more interesting.

"Interesting?" queried Monsieur le Curé. "Now there you have a superb, a truly superb Satanic delusion!"

"Stifle your surprise," said Jan, "but for once I'm inclined to agree with you."

"Mon Dieu!" breathed Monsieur le Curé. "Then this *is* an occasion!"

Marie-Thérèse said she'd say it was, but in so fervent a voice that Jan said all right, he'd admit he never lightly declined a promising opening to any good argument, and that he and Monsieur le Curé therefore spent many an agreeable evening disagreeing about everything under the sun, but nevertheless the truth was the truth. . . .

Here he paused; and nothing, simply nothing, could have been more dramatic.

"Well, go on?" urged Marie-Thérèse. "Don't overdo the suspense! Can't you see you have us all suffocating nicely with curiosity?"

"Well, if you must know," said Jan, "it was a man I once met when I was working in Italy. Yes, yes, when I was a fine Sworn Translator there. I spent my first holiday in Rome, of course. And I'd been sight-seeing all day, but now I was sitting outside a café, enjoying my coffee, just as we are doing now, when I became aware of a stout gentleman at the next table to mine, a gentleman in a smart pale blue suit, pensively sipping a long drink.

"By and by, a real Fra-Angelico of a lad came round,

selling picture postcards, maps, guides and souvenirs. And I was just about to settle on a model of the Leaning Tower of Pisa when the pensive gentleman leaned towards me.

"'Excuse me, Signor,' he said in excellent French, 'but you would do well to offer that young brigand exactly half what he is asking.'

"So I did; and Fra Angelico gave the gentleman a truly Neapolitan scowl, but promptly accepted the reduction.

"'No, no, don't thank me!' sighed my benefactor. 'I can't sit by and see you fleeced. At least not to-night; to tell the truth, I'm feeling extremely peculiar.'

"He leaned still nearer.

"'I've just been to Confession,' he said, 'the first time in thirty years, though I don't know why in the devil I'm telling you so, except of course that you're a complete stranger and I'm not likely to set eyes on you again.'

"So I murmured something about ships that pass in the night, and that I supposed he meant he was feeling peculiarly lighter and brighter.

"And he said well, yes, and no. Definitely no, as well as yes. And that was precisely why he was feeling so very peculiar.

"Deeply interested, I called for drinks for us both, and waited to hear more.

"And he said that both his parents had died when he was a baby in the cradle, and that he'd been brought up by his maternal grandmother.

"Very gentle and pious, his granny. And gently determined to make him very pious, too.

"So every Saturday God gave, she sent him off to Confession.

"He said I wouldn't think so to look at him now, but he'd been a highly sensitive and imaginative child. And he'd kneel there in his village church picturing all the bright Saints of Heaven, just as they were painted on the walls around him.

"And it would seem to him that the moment they caught sight of him kneeling there, they would push back their shining haloes and yawn:

" 'Here he comes again, that poor Beppé!'

"Yes, he was convinced that he must always sound infinitely boring to their celestial ears, he and his little list of sins, always the same no matter how hard he strove to be different, always the same, Saturday after Saturday.

"But he was like all other children—he never spoke these secret thoughts of his to anyone.

"Then one day he came across an old prayer-book that had belonged to his great-grandmother, a massive book with gold edges and a tarnished, rusty clasp. He managed to undo this, and the musty book fell open at the Exercise for Confession. With eyes popping out of his young head, he began to study the closely-printed Examination of Conscience, and he was just spelling out: 'Have you consulted necromancers?' when the book was snatched from him, and there stood his granny, sharply saying this was not a prayer-book for little boys. And she did up the clasp, and locked the book away in a cupboard.

"She didn't know what she had done, of course, but it was then that Beppé realised there must be sins about so bad and black that the list was kept in great prayer-books with stout clasps. And every Saturday he would kneel in his quiet church and wish and wish he'd had the luck to consult a necromancer or something else frightful, just to make those yawning saints jerk bolt upright and gasp, 'Mamma mia! Do you hear what I hear? Is it possible? Can that be our timid little Beppé?'

"But as he grew older, he gradually forgot all these strange fancies. Indeed his conscience must have been something of a child-prodigy for it simply did not stand up to adult life. Beppé candidly admitted that he had knocked round the world coldly telling himself one has only one life to grab all one can. So he grabbed—and with both hands.

"Now that week-end, business had brought him to Rome. And when evening came, he thought he would take a good walk to work up an appetite for his dinner and night-club.

"Now there's something about an evening in Rome, especially when the sun sets behind the great dome of Saint Peter's, and a thousand bells begin to ring and sing, filling all the air with music, catching at the strings of every heart as it soars up and up.

"And before he realised it, there was our Beppé walking up the steps, and into Saint Peter's.

"A hundred little lamps were burning in the gloom, and something swept over him—he could almost hear his old granny crying, 'Oh, Beppé! Beppé! At last!'

"And before he had time to stiffen, her gentle little ghost took him by the arm and fairly pushed him into the nearest confessional.

"But half-way through his sordid catalogue, he came to a sudden halt. And he could have wept—but not with contrition. No, no, it was something far more poignant than that. It positively gripped him by the throat, and he heard his unseen confessor saying: 'But continue, my son, continue!'

"So he continued, but all the while he was seeing those bright Saints of his childhood, haloes pushed back . . . striving their celestial best to stifle their yawns, their weary yawns.

"And there among them stood Beppé the child, dark eyes brimming with tears to hear how tedious, dirty and wearisome was this Beppé the Sinner!"

Nobody spoke for a moment. Then Monsieur le Curé leaned over the table, and warmly shook Jan's hand.

"For once," he said, "I am speechless, save to ask if you ever saw this Beppé again."

"No," said Jan. "I looked out for him, but I never came across him again."

My husband thoughtfully remarked that maybe it was just as well.

"Yes, perhaps," said Jan.

"Alas!" said Monsieur le Curé. "I only wish I, too, was not obliged to agree."

"Ah no!" cried Marie-Thérèse, springing to her feet and beginning to collect the cups. "This makes twice in one hour we are all of one mind! What an evening to remember!"

"Yes, indeed," said my husband. "Can't say when I enjoyed one more."

Very late that night my husband paid them even a warmer compliment. He was getting into bed when he suddenly gave a quiet chuckle.

"Can you beat it?" he said. "We've just spent six hours sitting on the hardest kitchen-chairs in all France and nobody darn-well noticed it!"

Chapter XX

GOOD FISHING HERE!

Now my husband not only enjoys good conversation, he is also an ardent angler. And Jan's postcards promising "Excellent fishing here!" had struck a most alluring chord. Indeed, fishing tackle made up far the larger part of my husband's luggage, and I had been obliged to point out, very firmly indeed, that even he could hardly expect to carry his favourite one-piece rod half over France and still expect to have all six feet ten inches of it at the end of our trip.

And it speaks volumes for the company at the Happy Sparrow that he allowed a whole week to slip by before he contrived to bring the conversation round to fishing. And he was just about to ask where the river was, when Jan cried, "Fishing! The man you want is Marius Tavat. Come on! We'll go there now, this very minute!" And he slapped his straw-hat on his head and fairly swept my husband off to call on Monsieur Tavat.

Monsieur Tavat, it seems, was enchanted to see them, and at once invited them into a parlour that would have gladdened the heart of our Izaak Walton. The walls were absolutely plastered with framed photographs of Monsieur Tavat proudly holding up prize catches, or Monsieur Tavat proudly standing by little tables covered with prizes for his catches.

And there were three large glass cases, one on the piano, one on the mantelpiece, and one on the sideboard, in which were enshrined the brightest and best of Monsieur Tavat's catches, stuffed and most artistically wired so that they appeared to be floating amid green rushes and water-lily stems.

When my husband had admired all this, Monsieur Tavat brought out glasses and a bottle of wine, and they settled down to an agreeable discussion that ranged from tackle to the sporting qualities of pike.

Monsieur Tavat then gave a vivid account of how he had hooked and landed every fish in all three of the glass cases.

My husband listened, entranced. This Frenchman was a fisherman all right. And when he paused for breath and to pour out more wine, my husband respectfully inquired what bait Monsieur Tavat would suggest for their river.

"A-ah! Bait!" said Monsieur Tavat, and in a voice that clearly indicated that this was his personal contribution to the Entente Cordiale, he gave my husband an infallible and secret recipe of his own invention, a balanced mixture of breadcrumbs, minced pig's liver, honey, garlic, and a pinch of fine sand, all moistened to a firm paste with a dash of strong beer. He then wrote all this down so that my husband would not forget any one of the vital ingredients.

Now my husband is a true Briton. He is not easily carried away. But all this excellent talk, and maybe the excellent wine, now soared to his head. Presently, he realised he was no longer listening. He was just sitting there, thinking most blissfully.

To-morrow, thought my husband, he would be standing

on the bank of that delightful river. He would cast his float
—a red-tipped quill—into the sparkling channels between
the swaying banks of that lush green weed so admirably
described by Monsieur Tavat.

To-morrow, he would skilfully flick that secret and
infallible bait in the deep, mysterious pool under the weir,
haunted, so Monsieur Tavat said, by a shoal of striped,
hog-back perch.

To-morrow, when evening fell, he would then plod his
happy way to that other quiet stretch, also warmly recom-
mended by Monsieur Tavat; and there he would angle for the
olive tench, the fat and lazy bream, amid the broad lily beds.

To-morrow, in the open creel at my husband's feet,
great shining fish would flap, long as his arm. And again
he would cast a gossamer line, and this time he would
land the fish of his dreams, the fish of which he could talk
. . . till Death did them part.

To-morrow, my husband would not change places with
a shining archangel.

To-morrow, my husband would be fishing.

And he heard himself ask, "By the way, where is your
river? I've not set eyes on it yet, you know."

Monsieur Tavat looked at my Cousin Jan.

My Cousin Jan looked at Monsieur Tavat.

Then they both looked at my husband; and sighed.

"Monsieur," said Monsieur Tavat, and swiftly refilled my
husband's glass, "as Jan here will tell you, in the autumn
and summer our river flows as swift and deep as your
River Thames. But . . . but . . .

He threw up desolate arms. "At this time of the year,
my poor Monsieur, it dries up! There's not a drop of
water left anywhere in it!"

Chapter XXI

OUR BELOVED OMA

Now I pride myself that I can cram as much news on the back of a picture postcard as anybody else in our family.

But it had simply not come into my head—even if I'd had the space—to explain on my card to Jan that we had decided to take our holiday in June for a variety of reasons—with economy heading the list. But presently we began to notice that every now and then somebody or the other would make a remark that sounded as if they thought we had sensibly timed our visit so as to be there on the twenty-fourth of June. But before we had time to ask why the twenty-fourth, the conversation had always swept on to something else.

Then we began to notice that bonfires were being built on the top of every likely hill for miles around. And these certainly were the most artistic erections, each one constructed round a central mast as it were—a great branch of a tree, the green leaves still fluttering from its top.

So one evening my husband remembered to ask Marie-Thérèse if the twenty-fourth wasn't some sort of local Guy Fawkes Night.

She threw up scandalised hands. She said the twenty-fourth of June might mean just Quarter Day to us over in England, where by all accounts we were on the chilliest

terms with our saints, even with poor Saint George himself,
or so she had heard. But to them the twenty-fourth of
June meant the Feast of Saint John; and in that village they
had a very special regard for Saint John. So naturally they
paid him the compliment of celebrating his feast-day.

And yes, those beautiful bonfires were being built by the
young people in honour of Saint John. They'd be lit as
soon as it grew dark on the great day.

"You may not have noticed it, of course," said my Cousin
Jan, "but nobody in their senses is leaving any spare
tomato or vine stakes knocking about just now. No wood,
you understand, is too good for Saint John. In fact we have
the very warmest opinion of him, as you will see."

Jan was right. That village certainly did pay its warmest
respects to Saint John on his feast-day.

The celebrations began with High Mass; and Marie-
Thérèse fairly hustled us off, declaring we wouldn't get a
chair if we weren't early. Now usually the floor of the
church was quite bare. There were no benches or pews,
but behind the door towered a crazy mountain of chairs.
An old lady mounted guard before this, rattling a tin into
which we all dropped a coin before we tore off a chair each
and carried it to any place we fancied. We knelt on one side
of these chairs, and got up and turned it round to sit down
on the other.

But by the time we arrived that festive morning, early
as it was, the church was fast filling up. Dense tangles of
chairs were already spreading out in all directions, and we
had to thread our way in and out, carrying our chairs
shoulder-high till we at last discovered an odd empty
corner.

And no sooner were we safely settled in than we heard

a distant poum-poum-POUM! Instantly the scraping of chairs, the rustling, the whispering ceased. Every head turned towards the door. And in marched La Sainte Cécile. And there, bringing up the rear, and walloping the drum in faultless style, was my Cousin Jan.

They had a circle of chairs reserved for them near the door, which they thoughtfully left wide open so that old Picard down the road, bed-ridden these three years, might enjoy the music, too.

I secretly thought this was a boon to us all, especially when La Sainte Cécile attacked Zampa with great volume and verve. But, suddenly, as I looked at their earnest, shining faces, I remembered the lovely old legend of Our Lady's Juggler, who also gave of his best to the glory of God. And very ashamed, I wondered if it would be better if we all had the sense to ask just this of ourselves . . . and left the rest to a merciful Heaven.

Then my thoughts wandered to Jan and Marie-Thérèse; how strangely they had come together; how warm and deep were their content, their love for each other.

And there was something else as well, something that even now I find hard to pin down in words.

"Then are they glad," sang the Psalmist, "because they be quiet; so He bringeth them unto their desired haven."

Maybe it was as simple as that; this inward quiet, the gladness that lit their desired haven like a lamp.

And I remembered how one evening when she and I were alone, Marie-Thérèse had said, "I have known what it is to be alone in the world, to realise that I did not matter to anyone. Believe me, it is the most terrible of feelings. Can you wonder I am so happy . . . now?"

"No," I said. "No."

And sitting there, in that crowded little church, I began to see what it was that so illuminated their happiness. It was a love, a tolerance, born of generosity, humour . . . and sorrow.

Well, now, for both of them, thank God, there was:

"Laughter and thought and friends."

And then I realised that everybody else was kneeling, so I hastily got up, turned round my chair, and knelt too.

When High Mass was over we all poured out into the warm sunshine again and watched La Sainte Cécile form up and march majestically off. All round the village they went, and then twice round the market-square, before they slung their instruments into the little bandstand, and went home to eat a well-deserved repast in honour of good Saint John.

Now the Café of the Happy Sparrow is, of course, right on the market-square. So we were able to eat and watch an army of perspiring gentlemen putting the finishing touches to the stalls, the two merry-go-rounds, and the other attractions now being rigged up, with much yelling and lively argument, all round the bandstand.

We were particularly interested in something that Marie-Thérèse called a "a mast of Cocagne"—a tall pole from the top of which dangled a couple of long sausages, two or three bottles of wine, and half a dozen or so packets of cigarettes. All free, to be grabbed by anyone prepared to pay a modest sum just to climb the pole. The only little drawback was that the pole was now being most generously smeared with soap, before erection.

Then Jan introduced us to a jovial gentleman who had his lorry parked behind the café, and who was now tearing to and fro with mysterious boxes for his rifle-range—the valuable prizes, no doubt. And from that moment on, every time this gentleman panted past, yelling, "Allez! Allez! Fichez-moi le camp!" to the children cluttering up his path, he would turn to us and roar, "Teem ees mooney, eh?"

So I asked Jan if this was some sort of Provençal war-cry. And Jan said certainly not, it was English, plain English.

So we worked it out and it *was* English. It was, "Time is money, eh?"

By two o'clock everything was ready. Behind every little stall stood a persuasive gentleman, megaphone at the ready. And La Sainte Cécile climbed up into the bandstand, and to the strains of "Toreador", the fête began.

And all that merry, sunny afternoon long, we strolled round, watching the cycle-race, the sack-race, the children on the merry-go-rounds, and trying our luck at everything—except the "mast of Cocagne". And my husband, I am proud to say, won a bottle of anonymous but Vintage Champagne at the rifle-range—at least the label swore it was vintage.

Being middle-aged, however, we crossed back about five o'clock to the Café of the Happy Sparrow, and sat down. And kind, understanding Marie-Thérèse immediately set a pot of tea before us, crying, "But wait a little moment! I have something else! A cack! I cut the directions from a magazine. A real English cack!"

And she flew back to fetch it. It was a cake, a first-class sultana cake. But we had to eat it with our teaspoons because she had soused it with rum to make it even more festive.

By and by, it grew dusk, and the mothers began to round up the children. And the valiant Sainte Cécile, who hadn't spared themselves all day, packed up their instruments; and a gramophone took over, with loud-speakers fixed high on the plane trees. And the gentlemen in charge of the stalls and the merry-go-rounds decided to call it a day too; and presently they packed up, and drove away. And everybody set to work to clear away the litter, and the gramophone struck up "Voulez-vous danser, grand-mère?" and the Grand Ball began.

And now on every hill we could see the bonfires burning; and every now and then we would hear the distant shouts and laughter of children.

But the gramophone played on and on; and round and round the empty bandstand the lovers still danced, caught up in a bright world all their own.

We had supper very late that night so that Jan and Marie-Thérèse might sit down and have it with us—"The Happy Sparrow" had been doing a roaring trade, of course.

But now the café was quiet and deserted; and there we sat, outside on the pavement, taking our time over our coffee, and a special little glass in honour of Saint John.

And one by one the stars came out, and danced in the warm dark sky. And the gramophone gave a weary whirr and ceased to play. And the lovers went strolling home, arms still about each other. And presently, the market-square, the whole village lay still and silent.

But up on the hills, the bonfires still flamed in the darkness and from far away voices still called and laughed.

"They're jumping over the fires now," said Marie-Thérèse. "It brings good luck."

"Good luck," said Jan. And something in his voice made us all look at him.

"It is we who have good luck," he said. "For we have found the place to live . . . so many friends . . . so much to do . . ."

Marie-Thérèse took his hand; and for a moment we were all silent. Then Jan spoke again.

"I have written to our cousins in Holland," he said. "And also to Philippe in Marseilles, and poor Paul's wife. And now I will tell you what I wrote. What I most desire. Yes, and Marie-Thérèse, we both desire it. Send all your children to us! Let them meet here, under our roof. It is a good place for a holiday. And it is fine for children to meet . . . as we did."

And oh, as he spoke, I saw her again in his eyes, heard her speak with his voice . . .

Our Dutch grandmother, our beloved Oma.